The Department

Other Phoenix Fiction titles from Chicago

A Use of Riches by J. I. M. Stewart
Bright Day by J. B. Priestley
The Good Companions by J. B. Priestley
Angel Pavement by J. B. Priestley

The Department

Gerald Warner Brace

The University of Chicago Press
Chicago and London

The University of Chicago Press, Chicago 60637
The University of Chicago Press, Ltd., London

90 89 88 87 86 85 84 83   1 2 3 4 5

Library of Congress Cataloging in Publication Data

Brace, Gerald Warner, 1901–
  The department.

  (Phoenix fiction series)
  Reprint. Originally published: New York: Norton,
1968.
  I. Title.   II. Series.
[PS3503.R14D4   1983]   813'.52   83-1197
ISBN 0-226-06968-0 (pbk.)

Some fifteen years ago I dedicated a novel to my colleagues and added a suitable text from Robert Browning. A few took kindly notice of my effort, and I was grateful. I should like to venture the same dedication again. In my long academic life I have been associated with generous and just and wise men and women. I have very great respect and affection for them.

Author's Note

In a cautionary apologue at the beginning of *Roderick Random* Tobias Smollett tells of a young artist who "sketched a kind of conversation-piece representing a bear, an owl, a monkey, and an ass, and to render it more striking, humorous, and moral, distinguished every figure by some emblem of human life." The artist was dismayed to find that his friends at once took it to be a lampoon upon themselves. "In vain," Smollett continues, "the astonished painter declared that he had no intention to give offence, or to characterize particular persons: they affirmed the resemblance was too palpable to be overlooked; they taxed him with insolence, malice, and ingratitude."

I hope no reader of the following pages is possessed by any such illusion. What is written is pure fiction. The characters exist for the purposes of the fiction. They have no other relevance or reference.

"Christian reader," Smollett goes on with feeling, "I beseech thee, in the bowels of the Lord, . . . seek not to appropriate to thyself that which equally belongs to five hundred different people. If thou shouldst meet with a character that reflects thee in some ungracious particular, keep thy own counsel; consider that one feature makes not a face, and that, though thou art, perhaps, distinguished by a bottle nose, twenty of thy neighbors may be in the same predicament."

AMEN.

The Department

For out of olde feldes, as men seith,
Cometh al this newe corn fro yeer to yere;
And out of olde bokes, in good feith,
Cometh al this newe science that men lere.

—The Parlement of Foules

⤳ CHAPTER 1 ⤳

I SLEEP WELL, mostly, but I compose farewell speeches. There is a long table, a private dining room in the faculty club, twenty or twenty-five there—am I at one end, or in the middle glancing right and left? A luncheon. Some of the eminent ones get a dinner, with deans and extra tables. Friends, colleagues, and then what? You can't be pompous. Modest, unaffected, informal, witty, charming, at ease as a speaker—and of course wise. That's how professors are, that's their business.

Not that it matters too much—the speech, I mean. It's a formality for anyone who retires. We try to be nice. We smile, gently applaud. There is a present, an edition of Ben Jonson, a piece of Steuben glass, a check—opened in view of all, with suitable cries of pleasure and gratitude. We are for a time united in awareness of mortality. Each one sees himself standing for the last time in the light, saying the last words. I keep beginning it—in the night, or when I am walking, or riding in a bus. "Friends, colleagues." But it isn't serious, or solemn. "I look forward at last to having time to get some

work done." Laughter. "For forty years I have tried unsuc-
cessfully to avoid committee duty. Now I intend to assert
myself." More laughter. We laugh easily at such times. It
conceals embarrassment. We assume for the occasion that retirement is a pleasure long anticipated, we envy the freedom,
the release from drudgery, the chance above all "to do my
own work." It is always supposed that every college teacher
has his own work to do; all through his life he lets it be
known that he is driven constantly by his assigned duties, his
big classes, papers, committees, but what he yearns for is
time to do "his work"—presumably an original and brilliant
piece of scholarly writing.

I see the faces down that long table—for some reason I am
standing at one end. I am pretty nervous about it. Friends,
colleagues—and enemies? Not really—I'm not important
enough to be an enemy, but by chance I had title and tenure
(I have them now) and they look upon me with that implacable professional criticism which is their habit. They judge
every word and gesture. Most wear spectacles, are pale from
the long indoor winter, rather tense—I see Fulmar blinking
and blinking with a twitchy little smile at the left side of his
mouth. My retirement does leave a gap, after all; someone
will move up. Not that the system works as literally as that,
but rank and tenure and salary are the prizes we strive for.
No betrayal on those faces—none of any sort. After all, I
know a good deal about them: you can't be with such a
group year after year without knowing them, but in truth
they all live and work with the caution of poker players.
They are all "authorities." Each one is presumed to know
more about something than anyone else. And they are all
masters of the world's wisdom. That's the professor's rôle: he
is supposed to know everything. He lectures, interrogates,

judges.

So I am nervous—I always am, specially in these presences. But I try not to betray myself. I allude casually to *Tristram Shandy*—I am supposed to be an authority on the eighteenth century novel. They chuckle agreeably; they do really try to be nice—except for McLoon whose face is set in a death-mask of disapproval. I refer to "my own work" with what I intend to be deprecating irony—after all, they know I haven't published anything in a long time but a few book reviews, and the chances of my producing any significant "work" are quite remote. I am in truth a poor sort of scholar, and they know it, but under the rules of our game I must never seem to admit it. We must pose—it is necessary. Jaeger, that formidable authority on the mysteries of Dickens's *Edwin Drood*, was always the most arrogant man in the department—but he published nothing, not even book reviews. At doctors' orals he always acted like the Grand Inquisitor. Was it all bluff? Who really knows? He got away with it. He was feared—and hated. I have been bluffing all my grown-up life, but comparatively I am an amateur.

Too little confidence, too little courage. What I admire are the people who can speak strongly and movingly on great occasions. How can they do it without choking? Athletes at moments of crisis too. I have seen the fans draw a finger across their throats to express contempt for the man who chokes-up, as they say—who fails at the crisis. There are simple passages of verse and prose I cannot read in public because my voice breaks, not only well-known bits of Shakespeare or Keats, but occasional paragraphs of Dickens, say, or Hawthorne. It seems ludicrous. I have lectured for thousands of hours, yet I am afraid to say "bare ruin'd choirs where late the sweet birds sang" because the words make me cry. I could take some pride in being sensitive, but the great actors who render great speeches are sensitive too, and in full control of all their faculties. If I were trying to play King Lear and had to say at the last "Pray you undo this button" I should simply blubber. But it doesn't seem to be sentiment that unmans me, or what we think of as beauty. I am not really sure what it is. The only term I can think of is felicity, a rather fancy word that makes its meaning out of its sound. In *The House of the Seven Gables* Hawthorne describes how a gaunt old spinster named Hepzibah Pyncheon gets dressed in the morning. A comic scene, but I am afraid to read it aloud.

It occurs to me often that if I retired a year or two before my time, with a minimum of fuss, I could avoid some of this farewell formality. I wouldn't be on hand for the occasion. But I don't admit to myself that I am that much of a coward. I was never a fighter, granted, and I suffer from too much sensibility, but I do stick to things, I persevere, as the old motto of the family proclaims. *I will persevere.* I remember too that when John Piper resigned suddenly about ten years ago we all shook our heads with a kind of ironic awareness that he had been hounded and scared by the tough young scholars who considered him a fossil.

But there's more to it than sensibility. It is a question of money. The longer I can stick with it the better my pension will be—and at best it is meagre. The main consideration, though, is Harriet. I have to live up to her vision. In theory, in her own concept of herself, she is a fighter, though her actual field of combat has dwindled to almost nothing: she can attack salesmen and clerks fiercely enough, but beyond that she has less and less to do with the real world. If she works at all, it is through me, whom she regards as in-

effectual and even pusillanimous. But since I am her link
with life, and she is part of mine, I must conduct myself with
her in mind. I should go into this subject at length, of
course, but I hate to plunge all at once. Marriage is a big territory.

As a matter of fact and record, I wrote and published a
novel some twenty-seven years ago, before I married Harriet.
It gave me my academic start. That plus a PhD from Harvard made me appear more promising than I actually was;
my failure to publish anything of importance since then is
simply a failure of character. The novel was considered respectable in its time, and is even now included in lists,
though no one reads it. I wanted to call it *A New England
Tragedy*, but I didn't have the nerve—and now I'm glad I
didn't. But I called it *Aftermath* and that's pretty dismal too.
The idea was to be dismal. I haven't actually read it in ten
years, or maybe twenty, and I really hope it is better than I
think it is, but I wrote it in what I suppose is the fashion of
perfectly conventional realism—and when it does appear on
a list it is lost among the Cathers and Whartons and Dor-
othy Canfield Fishers. In a way it is what critics call derivative (which means imitative), but the stuff of it came
straight out of the lives of my father's father and mother in
Allensville, Vermont—or at least out of their farm on the
side of Stafford Mountain. I used to stay with them in the
days of its prime—or what as a child I supposed was its
prime, with all its cattle, horses, mowings and plowings.
They died together, the farm and the old ones, and the life
and world of six generations came to an end. Is it a too obvious and familiar motive? I was moved strongly at the time.

But I was thinking of the territory of a novel—of what is
encompassed by marriage, for example. Forests and swamps

and ranges. It is all very well to let the mind fly over it, but the writer has to go physically into it, inch by inch, like Lewis and Clark on the trail to Oregon. I put it off. I keep thinking about that insignificant speech. Friends, colleagues.

"Since this is my last chance at a captive audience, I ask your indulgence. You aren't used to listening, of course, so I'll be as brief as I can." (Agreeable chuckles and smiles, except for McLoon.) "But . . ."

But what? Here you are, boldly standing, facing the authorities, the wise and learned pundits. This is your chance to say, to speak. Do you utter a few serious thoughts? Or do you stick with the urbane clichés?

The trouble with serious thoughts is that everybody has them, reads them, knows what they are. Is anything ever new in the philosophical world? Journals, magazines, discussions go on week upon week forever. You can't tell these boys anything. They've heard it all—and Plato said it first anyway. Yet there's an article of faith among teachers that the key to all cultural good lies in the word communication. They quote the novelist Forster with almost a tone of unction: "Only connect." Instead of the amateurish term "discussion" they now say "dialogue," as though that achieved more profound truth. If a man of words gives up his respect for the efficacy of words he gives up everything.

Which is what I am almost ready to do. I am tired, or lazy. Any honest utterance is a sort of Lewis and Clark plunge into wild country. It is hard work, and dangerous. People like me would rather stay safe and easy in the settlements.

"But there are one or two things—if you'll bear with me a moment . . ." No, that's too damned humble. I may be modest enough in reality, but putting on the pose of modesty is a habit I indulge in—as most of us do: though what is and what isn't pose is beyond all analysis.

Tell them a story, for God's sake. Tell them one about Kittredge of Harvard—that always goes big with professors. We were doing *Hamlet*, and in the middle of one of his disquisitions Kittredge heard the rustle of a newspaper. He paused. There was a dread silence. He surveyed the class. He said—

I'm not much on stories, actually. I've probably told that one on Kittredge anyway. I realize now that you have to make a business of finding and learning funny stories—you can't just expect them to generate in your mind. I tell that to my daughter Joan so that she can train her boys properly—I tell her that any young man who has a fund of available stories is destined for success. Joan herself is no better at them than I am.

Is it my life's history that I really want to tell to those men? Am I being impelled by that desire? It may be so—and why it should be I can't say. Perhaps every obscure man wants to be seen and known. Here for all to recognize is Robert Sanderling, doctor of philosophy, professor of English, sixty-odd years old, not really a celebrity, but a man of some culture, unconvicted of crime or public sin, author of one dull but very respectable novel, owner of property in Newtonville, faithful attendant at all faculty and committee meetings, occasional attendant at church (Congregational) and club meetings— Much more, of course, but in a way much less also. To be married to a difficult woman (who will never read this if I can help it), to be a father and grandfather, to live frugally without debt, to own a Ford Falcon several years old—is such a human history worth setting forth? Making a farewell speech out of it is preposterous, but what of a book—a novel, of course, since if I get into it at all

I shall have to do it that way? This pretended speech of mine is merely a day-dream after all.

Is there any point, really, in trying to tell so simple a story? Writers over the last century (since George Eliot, I guess) have been advising each other to make use of the humblest and most ordinary details. In one of Gissing's novels there's a character named Biffen whose ambition it is to write a novel called *Mr. Bailey, Grocer,* in which the truth will be told about the life of an utterly commonplace man, and not very long afterward we meet that average sensual resident of Dublin, Leopold Bloom. But it is absurd of me to go in for literary talk like that—it marks me as a teacher, and it shows me up as derivative. It is all old stuff, anyway. When you lecture on the novel you devote long hours to what you call the Rise of Realism. If you get along far enough you come to a period you label Beyond Realism, which is roughly where we are now. But the label doesn't do you much good.

I should still suppose that Bailey and Bloom are valuable characters, but let's not be sentimental about them, or superstitious. It is all very well to express a tender respect for the humble folk who lie in unvisited tombs, as most of us must in time, but the record of such lives can be very dull indeed. Nine tenths of truth is dull. Robert Sanderling is nine tenths dull.

But one knows that the elusive tenth may not be dull at all, that it contains the strangeness that fiction is always looking for. The last little twist of candor—we seldom reach it or see it.

≈§ CHAPTER 2 ≥≈

THIS SPRING it was Partridge's turn.

He belonged to an old era of rhetoric and oratory, and I doubt if many can remember as far back as that. No doctor's degree, but he was a proud and formidable man, and took on all challengers and upstarts. He knew what he knew. He was always on the side of the right. You may not remember his era, but you know his type. Son of a missionary, born in China (a China of ancient history), but a devout New Hampshire man whose ancestral Partridges lived in and about Jaffrey for centuries—all Dartmouth men. Immense native pride and virtue. These were the honest good people with rocky land under them and God close above them. He is up there now, in the old Partridge homestead, at ease with his conscience.

During his forty years in the university he lived in West Newton, not far from us, and always considered me somewhat of a kindred spirit. He assumed that I naturally subscribed to his view of God and virtue, and that I lived like him in a condition of daily rectitude. The fact that my

21

grandparents were Vermont farmers gave me great credit in his eyes: we were two old-timers together, with the same uncompromising standards. And my other grandfather was a Congregational clergyman too. My credentials in his eyes were the best. But I was in continual fear that he would "find me out"—and what that means, and why, is the motive of much of my speculation.

I meant to say, though, that his West Newton house was a pretty grim emblem of the man and his life—and perhaps of mine too, since it had a dreadful familiarity for me. The whole thing was a cluttered collection of the brown-plush relics of a dead world. The house was mostly roofs and porches, the rooms sunless and dark. Parlors, sitting rooms, dens, all full of a mixture of oriental and Victorian junk, all precious symbols of what the Partridges conceived of as cultural and moral virtue. I suppose his superiorities were as evident to him as the daily rising of the sun. He knew his own virtues, his ancestral virtues, his successes as student and teacher and rhetorical authority, his honorable rôle as son, husband, father, grandfather, his courage and faith, his devotion to the moral law, to plain living and old-fashioned tradition, to the modest humors of the generations of honest country folk who had produced him.

Yet he was almost buried under the debris of a hundred years. What-nots and hat-stands and Chinese screens (no doubt valuable) and marble tops and carved walnut and gilt picture frames and fake Persian rugs and blown-up family photographs (some in color) and massive book cases with glass doors and classics by the yard. Culture in a big way. I knew about it. My father's house was like that—in a second-class fashion, with less weight and gloom. My house might even have been that way—old Partridge was right in claiming me for a kindred spirit—but Harriet had other notions of domestic art, and waged personal war on what she called funereal junk. I've seen her almost break her toe in a fury of kicking a great mahogany contraption we used to own, and I realize that right was mostly on her side: but she can be a difficult woman, as I have said.

Florence Partridge may have been difficult in her own way, but her rectitude was even more immense than his. After all, he could be a jester, even a wit; he could recite funny poems almost unceasingly—"John Gilpin's Ride," "Skipper Ireson," "The Biglow Papers," "The Courting," "The Hunting of the Snark," the whole of Gilbert and Sullivan. At parties he was formidable. But Florence expressed nothing but sober and unalterable righteousness. She had a battleship look to her, a large chin and nose, a mass of white hair like an armored parapet above her forehead, and a fortified bosom. She offered no ideas, and seldom altered her steadfast expression, but he deferred to her, honored her with absolute respect, considered her the living repository of all the dynastic virtues and glories of the Partridges. She dusted the relics every day. Partridge actually referred to them as the *lares et penates*, but lightly, as part of his cultural humor.

All this is pretty familiar to old-fashioned New Englanders. There used to be many Partridges—specially many Florence P's. He, Simon P., was an exceptionally able man. He recited all those poems to illustrate his extraordinary memory, and he could rattle off dates and presidents and kings and everything else that he had ever heard about. Back in the days of those TV quiz shows he was as excited as a boy, and was right on the verge of competing and winning a fortune when the whole thing blew up in charges of dishonesty—and of course he was implacable in his condemnation of all the culprits. It was specially reprehensible for a scholar to involve himself in any such wickedness because a scholar is trained primarily in integrity and owes his allegiance to truth above all.

He could say things like that, with fervor and energy, and you liked him for it. No unction, no pose—it was just obvious common sense. That's where we differ—I pretty much agree with him, but I can't say it with that kind of conviction. I see myself in that boat. Suppose they dangled a fortune in front of me. How good is my integrity? Suppose, suppose . . . .

There are things I must conceal—not big things, perhaps (I never had a chance at a fortune), but little soft slippery slimy things. What's the dirt, people ask you, trying to be bright and amusing. There's always a line to draw, a door to shut, a dirty little secret to keep. Perhaps even Partridge had a few of his own, but if you can say of any man that his life was an open book you can say it of him.

He was our chairman for ten years or so. He was very good at it, of course, but the problem was how to get rid of him. Any man who considers William Vaughan Moody to be the great American poet of the twentieth century is in no condition to be the chairman of a university English department—that I take it is an acceptable premise. Partridge's taste crystallized about nineteen fourteen. He just barely accepted Edwin Arlington Robinson, partly as a fellow New Englander of understandable origins. Not Frost, though—not with any warmth. No principles in Frost, he said. Too much equivocating. And too much plain language. How could anyone trained in the great traditions of Milton—and so on. Comic verse was all very well in its place, and he admitted that Frost was pretty good at that—he could do to perfection the one called "Farmer Brown's Descent, or the Willy-Nilly Slide," with the right country accent, but Great Poetry sounded to him like a ritual to be intoned in a church. And being funny or even ironic about God, as Frost was in *A Masque of Reason*, seemed blasphemous to him.

You can see how embarrassing all this would be in an up to date English department, where the prevailing attitude is sardonic and morally uncommitted. Not that I am up to date either, but I see how things are, I tend to be a watcher from the sidelines, whereas he fought the good fight—and lost, at least in the eyes of his colleagues and a good many students. His course in American poetry had once drawn hundreds, and slowly dwindled, and the knowing ones derided it, called it Salvation by Poetry, or Moody and Sankey Forever. Not fair, cruel in fact, but that's what the modern temper is. How do you tell an able and confident veteran that he is no longer satisfactory? He is the chairman, the "chief" as he liked to hear himself called, he is Professor Simon Partridge, one of the Jaffrey Partridges, Dartmouth man, Phi Beta Kappa, MA, Columbia, pillar of his church, well-known speaker at clubs and honorable occasions, author of *Rhetoric for College Students* (1928). In his own world a very formidable man, and recognized as a chairman of great administrative efficiency.

I wasn't really in on the blow-up, but I know he took it like the thorough-bred he really was. His principles were large humanistic ones; he didn't indulge himself in personal resentments. If presidents and deans approached him with sober and just authority, he heeded and obeyed—though he altered in no way his own principles. The great moral war is going badly, he said. We are adopting the evil doctrine that Pope stated: "Whatever is is right." Nothing could be more pernicious, but it seems to be the basis of modern scholarship and criticism.

Naturally they handled it with extreme tact and unction. Most university executives recognize that teachers and scholars are vain, touchy, and fantastically self-important. A young anthropologist who publishes a paper on the conjectural dating of an australo-pithecine jawbone considers himself quite above the reach of the commonplace administrators who sit in offices and hire and fire underlings. Any competent philosopher is in touch with the wisdom of the ages, and one with Plato and Spinoza and Kant; it is preposterous to treat him as though he were simply a hired teacher. As for a major character like Simon Partridge—I certainly wouldn't have nerve enough to tackle him. That's one of the reasons I'm not a president or dean, who whatever abilities he may have or not have needs nerve above all. And tact too, though that isn't universal. But I'm sure ours did their best. They were afraid he was over-working. They wanted to give some of the younger men a chance to work in their special fields—there was Bunting who had done a brilliant book on Wallace Stevens (I'm pretty sure neither president nor dean, nor Partridge himself, had read more than a page or two of Bunting's book—and I know that Partridge had no use for Wallace Stevens at all). Actually they felt that he (Partridge) could be uniquely helpful in what really amounted to a crisis in the area of debating. The Department of Speech had fallen on hard times, and needed a strong hand—and Professor Partridge's courses in logic and argumentation were celebrated in the academic world. . . .

He retained his course in Victorian prose, and enlisted a small band of the faithful. If I haven't given the impression that he was a charming and magnetic man I have done him wrong. His brisk, confident, honest mind functioned delightfully, and he stood up proudly and squarely, a somewhat chunky man with fine white hair and pink skin.

At the farewell gathering this spring he was in his element, and somehow you realized the magnitude of his career. He belonged to all sorts of clubs and societies, was an officer of this and an honorary of that. He had been in the First World War, had won a medal in France, and had reappeared in the Second as a temporary colonel in charge of logistic operations of some sort—all this came to us impressively. I don't know about the others, except that in the eyes of some he was no scholar, and therefore of no real significance in our world, but I acutely felt the meagreness of my own life in comparison to his. When my honors are memorialized, what can they say?

As a man of faith and pride, he faced his test with buoyant energy. He had an orator's voice that could easily dominate a conversational group (again and inevitably I compared myself to my own disadvantage) and he knew how to speak with conviction, even on the most trifling matters. I sat some distance down the table from him, but I could hear his resonant crisp voice, full of confidence in whatever it was saying—he spoke, I remember, about the dogs in the Chinese village where he lived as a child, and how cruelly they were treated and what a mean and vicious lot they were, and he moralized on human cruelty east and west. It almost seemed, he said, that nature herself abhorred kindness: he'd been reading an article about the breeding habits of birds on an island off Labrador where it looked as though a sort of genocide was an inevitable part of the cycle—and there were some who assumed that the same was true of mankind, or should be true. He was a stout Christian, of course, and would have gone on to justify Christian compassion if someone hadn't diverted him into an anecdote about Mark Twain at Dublin, New Hampshire, where he was on his home ground. With his genius for remembering details he could go on forever. There was the McDowell colony, there was Robinson . . . .

And he handled his presents with such aplomb that you felt he was giving a professional performance. A pigskin briefcase with a first edition of *Past and Present* tucked inside it: "You've got me dated, all right," he said. "My past—and my present too." He held the book aloft, relishing the little ripple of appreciation. Any chance for a pun filled him with delight, not so much because he had what I would call a natural sense of humor as because he loved to score little points: he was a demon at puzzles and games and brain-twisters. He was always apt to whip out six matches and ask you to do something apparently impossible with them, and he was famous for being able to write his name on a blackboard with both hands at once—a trick he invariably performed for the astonishment of his classes (the left hand wrote the name from right to left, the right hand from left to right).

I suppose it is confidence that holds an audience. Partridge's thanks and valedictory sentiments seemed very important as he uttered them. He said friends, colleagues, and honored associates with such vibrant sincerity that I for one felt a clutch of emotion at my throat—yet he said it with just the right lift of sporting humor. "Whether you come to praise Partridge, or hopefully to bury him, I am indeed grateful. But seriously, it is no mere flight of fancy when I say that I am deeply touched. Notwithstanding my name, which I am of course foolishly attached to, I am not so bird-witted as to fail to realize how very fortunate I have been—in my work and opportunities here, and most of all in my colleagues.

When I look back over the years . . ."

In old carnival terms they call it a pitch, and it is a good word. Tone, accent, vibration—he had it all. He was as honest as a man can be, yet you could see how a man of similar equipment could have succeeded as a TV salesman of cigarettes or toothpaste or deodorants. It scares me to think how susceptible I have always been to the effective pitch. I know well that Partridge was a conscientious Christian, yet he took great pride in his performance; he summoned up sentiments of loyalty, tradition, dedication to all the noble aims of our profession, he remembered the great men of old, the brave ventures that led on to success, the modest but effective rôle that he himself had the good fortune to play. He ranged himself on the side of the Christian soldiers, and then warmly included all of us in the campaign. He resoundingly quoted his favorite poet, Browning, and assured us that though he might be retiring from the front lines he would never give up his dedication to the cause of Christian virtue.

I recognized his skill, but I was moved; the lump in my throat was quite palpable. I was grateful that he restored the balance at the end by inviting us one and all to visit the old nest of Partridges in Jaffrey, where we would doubtless find him sitting at ease in his pear tree. But he had given us the impression that he would prefer death to a life of ease: he could hardly wait to get at "his work," and he seemed to assume that we naturally knew what his work was. We all knew that he was an implacable enemy of Webster's Third International Dictionary, and was piling up munitions and arms for an all-out attack—no opportunity passed, at lunch or in committee or faculty rooms, that he didn't produce some little illustration of the pernicious folly of the professional linguists. So I presume that will be "his work," but I know that most of his energy will go into maintaining his lawns and gardens and seeing to the preservation of his house and the Partridge possessions.

My habit, as you see, is a bit evasive. I admire good men and good deeds—I believe in them, which many are unable to do, but I stand away from them; my rôle is vicarious. "The trouble with you, Sanderling, is that you think little." McLoon actually said that once. It was at one of the department parties given by the Medricks, he being our rich col· league with a big house in Cambridge, and McLoon was half drunk on Scotch and thought he was being affable—the only time he addressed me at all was when he had had three or more drinks. I know what he meant about thinking little, and under the circumstances I couldn't resent it—in fact it is exactly the sort of truth that is induced by alcohol. "That's Scotch wit," I said to him, but since he never listened to anything I said he didn't respond further. Poor McLoon—he looks just like an old Scotsman in one of Smollett's novels but is infinitely sadder. As I watched Partridge at the close of his speech, smiling buoyantly at the applause, I could see McLoon's gaunt death-mask of a face diagonally across the table from me—not a flicker of affability on it, nothing but downward-cutting lines and features and the drooping hairs of a sandy mustache. I guess he resented Partridge's well-being—or anyone's. But the fact is that I was really excited by the whole performance, by the confident eloquence, the appropriate puns and word-play, the sight of that physical and moral assurance standing before us, most of all by my belief in the Partridge chain of being, the linked generations of virtuous and strong characters. One son, Simon the Fourth, had so far done no more than make a good living in insurance, but the younger one, Francis, was out in East Pakistan doing prodigious deeds to control disease and pestilence.

So when I drifted out of the room afterward, with Jaeger and Fulmar and some of the others, I remarked that it had been one of Partridge's great performances. He'll surely be missed, I said. He represents something very fine. I knew as I spoke that what I said was fatuous. You don't intend to utter platitudes—at least I don't, but when I open my mouth they pop out. I felt foolish.

"Just the man," Jaeger said, "for an old-time school of oratory. That gesture with the left arm is one of their classic moves."

"Notice the weight distribution and foot-work," Fulmar said with the twitch of mouth that looked like a smile but really wasn't. "You got that in the second lesson."

This sort of thing happens all the time in academic circles. You can laugh appreciatively. You can say nothing. You can take issue, which may lead to serious consequences. Or you can go on with the game: the vibrato and tremolo, you can say, surely come in the advanced courses.

I couldn't take issue, not at a time like this (though one or two of my earnest colleagues might have done so—Grosbeck, for example, who follows his own rational way regardless of all current attitudes). I couldn't cleverly go on with the game—to tell the truth I was a little hurt, as I always am at such times. So I said nothing, though I may have smiled nervously, with an effect of vagueness as if I hadn't quite taken in what they were so amusingly saying.

Partridge was one who rated more than a departmental lunch. An evening dinner came later, with an illustrious company of officials, old colleagues, former students, debaters, and Partridge outdid himself in oratorial effectiveness, but most of the younger men of the English department were not there.

CHAPTER 3

I MUST PRESENT more of these colleagues of mine. The problem that really bothers me is the problem of faith or "belief," as we say, among responsible people. We are all supposed to be responsible, goodness knows, but as society is now arranged college teachers are the custodians in charge of all major affairs.

I say this with deliberation. The clergy may devote themselves to the great social and moral problems, but in the main they follow the paths laid out in the academic departments of philosophy and sociology. And in truth their influence on the world is minor—at least it is minor in the areas of life I am familiar with. Political leaders talk big about responsibilities, as they must, but our reaction is often cynical.

Who else leads us?

The professor has become the universal expert. He stands behind the seats of power. He directs economic thought, political thought, scientific thought, and he takes charge of education and morals and all psychological matters. Of everything, in fact. When a grocery business wants to build new stores, they hire one of our professors to tell them where the profits will be highest. That's a function of geography.

This all began when the bomb was invented and used. Science won the war, and scientists were professors. It may seem obvious and axiomatic, but it struck me very strongly then, and more as time went on. At first it seemed to be the exclusive business of physicists, but now everything from juvenile morals to the location of supermarkets is part of the scientific dominion—and even departments of art and literature and philosophy are staffed more and more by research scientists. As an individual I may be somewhat anachronistic, but as a professor I find myself a member of a dominant élite who are looked upon as the leaders and saviors of the future. People call me "doctor" with an almost pathetic respect, and assume that I can elucidate the principles of modern art—and by logical extension the manners and morals and behavior of the young.

To say that professors are mostly "good men" is hardly useful, though I believe it is true. Many cynics and young novelists assume the worst about them, and some students are eager in digging up what they call dirt, but I am convinced that most of my colleagues are more conscientious than I am, and certainly more competent. But the difference between outward appearance and inward reality is nearly always greater than I, at least, suspect. Now and then I see some grim "truth" I had been blind to—more often than not under-cover sex among the younger ones, but I think the true weakness of most college teachers is related to vanity and the consequences of vanity.

There's our chairman, George Willett, who is eligible to retire a year or two after I do. I say eligible because the logistics of retirement are always uncertain: some men depart quickly, others stay indefinitely. It is all too confusing to explain. A chairman is supposed to be the head man in a department, and is given a good salary and other perquisites, with a big office and a secretary, and is treated very respectfully by the administration and the public. But his colleagues take other attitudes. They are grateful to him for doing the dirty work. They resent it that he has certain powers of decision, specially about who gives what courses. They criticize him for sacrificing his scholarly work, and declare that no honest scholar would ever accept a chairmanship. They count on him to represent them honorably and effectively in all public or administrative encounters, and are very quick to find fault with him. But mainly they want to like him and get on with him—and they want him to leave them alone.

In any group of thirty or forty (or more) there are always a few ambitious politicians who like titles and can't resist trying to run things. They can be obnoxious, of course, but in general they are invaluable. They sit on committees, draw up programs, make reports, make motions, keep in touch with what they refer to as "the latest thinking" on methods of education. Willett is such a one. He is a natural administrator, and is known to have declined two offers of presidencies from small colleges; I think we all assumed he would become one of the university deans, if not something bigger—and I am sure he was expecting it too. He is sixty-two or three now. But he looks no more than forty-five, except that his hair is pure white. He is a beautiful man, too beautiful to be a professor: the blond glow of his youth remains with him, the smooth pinkish skin, the blue eyes, white teeth, ready smile. He stands erect, still slim and flexible, and speaks cheerily with manly candor. He is probably too handsome to succeed on the highest levels: he inevitably looks like an actor hired for the part.

I suppose this physical elegance implies great vanity, but it is fair to say that Willett handles himself very well. He was brought up to be a gentleman and sportsman in the old ivy-league tradition, and learned the ways of good manners and modesty. He has a kind of wit, or quickness of mind, but little humor; he takes his administrative duties very seriously, and is respectful and tactful to the lowest as well as the highest. Most of us are glad to let him run things. And his office has a varsity glamor to it, with framed photographs of Fitzgerald and Hemingway and Stein and others he had known in Paris in his youth—and also a Princeton hockey team with Willett standing shoulder to shoulder with the great Hoby Baker. How well he knew all the celebrities is never clear to us, and he is a difficult man to make fun of: his worldly man-to-man candor is really an impenetrable defense. He does suggest that he and Fitzgerald were once close friends and kindred spirits, and at times is willing to talk about the tragedy of Fitzgerald "very seriously." He always refers to him as Scott.

His true vanity lies in his attitude toward scholarship: he regards himself as a sort of varsity scholar. He is "very serious" about it. He attends all the professional meetings, and is seen in the best company. In any discussion of policy he uses the words "scholarship" and "research" with an accent of religious reverence. It is true that many others do the same, and it may be that I am inclined to be too frivolous about the major business of my profession—and obviously I feel a bit self-conscious and inferior. In all departmental affairs the word scholarship hovers over us like a divine emanation. But Willett makes obeisance to it with a fervor that is almost embarrassing. He is always pronouncing such phrases as "at the doctoral level" and "original research" with a solemn vibration of voice as though he were a high priest doing his office. And I must say it is probably a good habit: scholarship is our work, and we might as well be fervent about it. But I can't help being sceptical about Willett. He is after all an actor—and when you say a man is an actor you say he is a poor actor, an "amateur" at it. We are certainly all actors, and all the world is a stage. But we do often play our parts badly, or even falsely. Willett plays the varsity part of his rôle perfectly, and he does his administrative work as though he were born to it. I think he teaches well too, and teaching (or conducting classes) is a purely histrionic task. But professional scholarship does not become him. He does no research, though he talks about it. His critical views are purely conventional. His writing has a committee-report quality. The only thing he has published is the introduction for a paperback volume of selected poems by Shelley which begins with the sentences: "For the serious reader of Shelley, only the complete edition of his poetry and prose will be adequate. This little volume. . . ."

Like all chairmen he complains that the heavy administrative load deprives him of any real opportunity to go on with "his own work," and he does manage to give the impression that his researches in the field of romantic poetry, now in abeyance, will some day be the talk of the profession. And of course he is reserving his memoirs of Fitzgerald and the Paris exiles of the twenties for the time of his retirement, though he has all the essential notes and journals in his files.

This is so typically the vanity of the professor that it may seem too self-evident to mention. But it lies upon us all like a shroud. Every young instructor must seem to be working on something "for publication" and no matter what the reality of his intentions are he must convey the look and attitude of one on the verge of producing something scholarly and new and significant. After my doctor's degree I had a good job as instructor in a famous New England college, and one of the senior men in the department asked me what I was working on. That is obviously a standard professional question—and a dangerous one. In my innocence I evaded it. I was actually working on a novel, but had no confidence in it or expectation that I'd ever get to the end of it. "Oh, this and that," I said foolishly. "Nothing very productive, I'm afraid." Of course when my appointment came up for renewal I was fired.

Willett asks that question of all the younger men. He does it with tact, with a kind of professional eagerness, as though he were gratified and impressed to hear of investigations of Anglo-Saxon inflections or the phonetics of Gerard Manley Hopkins. He uses a pipe gracefully—has a rack of pipes on his desk with other collegiate symbols. "You know Hawkes of Cornell," he will say. "He has done a good deal of work in that field." He always knows who the authorities are. He is helpful, encouraging, very friendly, and of course the encounter, as far as the younger man is concerned, is as deadly as an ambush in a guerilla war. His professional future may depend wholly on the conclusions that are arrived at by affable pipe-smoking Professor Willett and later conveyed to the committee on appointments.

All this is routine. Judgments must be made, one way or another, and some are chosen, and others are rejected. Willett is certainly as fair as he knows how to be, and his respect for productive scholarship is genuine. His respect for all accepted values is genuine.

If you ask a man what he "believes in" he usually responds with a prepared statement. So far as he knows, it may be the truth. I am not one of those who think we can define "truth" in any ultimate way: we live and die among illusions as best we can. But as I said, I am part of a profession that has had leadership thrust upon it—and here for one example is George Willett, who is leading us. His field is literature, but he seems to take no delight in it, nor enter imaginatively into its world. He looks upon it rather as a collection of very important "material" which he and all of us must handle authoritatively. Our task is to codify it, get it organized in periods with appropriate labels, take special note of influences and sources. His own special task is to get hold of and encourage the scholars who can carry on the organizing process.

As for the matter of "value" and personal insight, I don't know: so far as I can tell he accepts whatever is respectable and current. If John Donne is the poet of the year, then Donne is his man. If the new critics go in for esoteric symbolism, he is all in favor of it, and displays the latest treatise on his office table. "You've seen Bannerman's new book, of course," he will say. "I can't accept some of it, but in the main it is quite brilliant." He says that about nearly everything he reads. He lets it be known that he is alert and eager in keeping up with the latest thinking. We all do the same; it is part of our vanity that we are up to date on all intellectual fronts. But Willett by virtue of his connection with Fitzgerald and the expatriates has very special modern obligations. He is devoted to Henry Miller, and is sponsoring a doctoral thesis by one of his students on Miller and the Paris exiles. You might doubt the respectability of this kind of thing, but if you do you are not in touch with current professorial thinking. We are on the whole afraid of making any "moral" judgments. We take the world as it comes, and let it be known that we are never surprised or caught off guard by the newest and latest.

I share these attitudes somewhat, but it seems evident that my conscience is not at rest. George Willett is an exceptionally able chairman; he is fair in his dealings, his ethics are those of a good sportsman, he encourages competence and "high standards," he has the speech and manners of a gentleman, and all in all he represents us better than we perhaps deserve. Is it reasonable to expect anything more? What I am probably looking for is a philosophy of some sort, or at least a guiding principle. Is this aim of "competence," whether scientific or pseudo-scientific, all we have?

Ordinarily we go along from day to day and year to year without troubling ourselves with questions. Here is the "material," we say. Study it, learn it, report it. We like the word; we use it constantly. "Material" may be old, new, original, questionable, essential—but whatever it is we deal in it. We encourage "sound scholarship" and the bibliographical techniques. I use these phrases because they echo from room to room in our department. And they imply a purely objective and clinical approach to the teaching of literature. They make scientists of us. And some of us are devoted to that science with single-minded dedication—Jaeger, for one, professes such devotion, and Grosbeck practices it. But Willett takes it for granted. We want to make sure, he tells all new instructors, that our majors learn sound scholarly methods; keep them up to the mark in all bibliography and reference work; check sources as much as you can. . . .

But with all his good will, his easy manners, his elegance, his pipe, he can't really put up with the eager young idealists who haunt all English departments—specially if they have beards. They can be a problem, of course. They return from Somaliland or Alabama with strong convictions about how to save people from persecution. The world's evil, they imply, is caused mainly by the stupidity of American politicians and bureaucrats, from the president down, and the university, like all our institutions, operates with equal stupidity. The solution, in their view, is to give freedom to all.

Perhaps I speak more ironically than I should. I don't know what their solution is, and I suspect that they have no conception of the evils inherent in human nature. But some of them demonstrate and "sit in" and carry placards, and some of them are very sweet and sensitive and courageous boys and girls. A few are mad, or on the edge of madness. And they are sometimes brilliant students, with the highest credentials, and we admit them to our graduate school and hire them as teaching fellows, as we call them.

Willett hates them. He keeps them out if possible, but they infiltrate. They are the poets and novelists and "creative writers," and Willett has got to the point where he equates creative writing with subversion. It is all very well for "accepted writers" like Henry Miller or Norman Mailer, say, to sound off in some far-out fashion—they are after all professionals of international fame, but when a bearded youth in our department suggests that the university, like the nation at large, is controlled by a group of wicked capitalists for their own perpetuation in power and glory, Willett is really furious. I suppose the truth is that he belongs to and in a way represents an old tory tradition. We don't much use the word tory any more, but it seems to fit the people like Willett who feel that they are hereditary gentlefolk with enough continuing prestige and property to give them special status.

They are very nice people, for the most part, and have been both deserving and lucky, but in these times they are defensive and afraid of change. According to Willett's view of himself he is tolerant and alert and intellectually adventurous; he had been Scott Fitzgerald's college companion, had played with him in the legendary times of Paris, had seen Joyce plain—and Stein and Hemingway (all dead now). He knows brilliance and genius when he sees them. But as for a pale, black-bearded, near-sighted young assistant named Mortimer Finkel who writes verse in scatalogical language and circulates it in mimeographed editions, Willett simply tightens his lips, shakes his head, and arranges to get rid of him. "Not really the sort we want here. Obviously not suited for work on a graduate school level. Have you seen this stuff he calls poetry? I don't know how Merlin puts up with it at all—I must really have a word with him." Merlin is our department poet, and encourages what some of us refer to as the beat fringe.

It is really difficult to define our feelings about creative and rebellious youth—and when I say "our" I do recognize a general attitude which I think exists. Between Willett on the one hand and Merlin on the other is a gulf of differences, but nonetheless the academic problem remains. We are all trained in the great humanistic tradition from Aristotle on through all the immortals of western culture—Dante and Chaucer and Shakespeare and Goethe and so on. That is what we teach. But now comes a rebellion against the humanistic tradition, against moral idealism, against reason itself, which for many centuries has been man's chief pride. How, to put it simply, does a professor deal with the extravagances of modern art?

Well, Willett and Merlin had quite a row. I was in on it

because I teach some of the creative writing too—by virtue of my novel of long ago. The Mortimer Finkels either laugh at me or scorn me—they don't even do me the honor of taking me seriously as a square. Of course they expect all professors to be prisoners of what they regard as a dead culture and they are sometimes sorry for us.

It is all preposterous, actually: the solemn devotion to irrational nonsense on the one hand, and the professed admiration for the mighty achievements of the human reason on the other.

Willett had the logical right of it. Mortimer Finkel was supposed to be a department assistant, which meant that he was allowed tuition in return for so many hours of work—mostly clerical, such as typing, filing, stuffing envelopes—and it was clear that Finkel was irresponsible, inefficient, and a "trouble maker," which meant that he talked too much and annoyed the more industrious workers.

Merlin noted that he was a poet, and you can't expect poets to be good at clerical work. As for talk, he probably talked well—he was a very original fellow.

Willett pointed out that he was getting a C in at least two of his courses and was always late with his papers. Merlin muttered something about a slavish addiction to letters, and Willett came back with a sharp little lecture on maintaining standards.

But the so-called poetry—can anyone seriously defend it? Willett waved at the typed sheets stapled to look like a thin book: he couldn't make head or tail out of the stuff, except that it was full of the filthy four-letter words you generally saw written on the walls of a men's room.

Merlin put up all the arguments. They are a form of truth, aren't they? The stuff, the ideas, all exist. It's part of life.

Young people all use the words. They are a normal part of their vocabulary.

Oh, come now? Nice girls . . . .

Merlin laughed. Willett flushed a bit.

Girls make a point of using the words. It is their freedom, their emancipation from genteel hypocrisy. They talk of sexual and bodily functions as they might talk of eating or drinking. A good thing, Merlin said.

You might as well advise us all to go naked, Willett said.

By all means, Merlin said. We'd be chilly, perhaps, but morally better off.

And the damn stuff makes no sense. It sounds like a dog yowling at the moon.

Well, there's some meaning to that, isn't there?

I assume we aren't dogs, after all.

Perhaps we can learn something from them.

So, you defend the man, do you? You think we should keep him on simply because he can yowl in filthy language?

Oh, come—that's not fair—

They both kept their tempers. Actually I don't think I ever saw Willett lose his. He was enough of a competitive athlete to know that when you lose your temper you lose the game. And I always admired his control. He could even stay polite and chivalric in battle.

I didn't know about Merlin. He was both very intense and very aloof, and from my point of view much too serious. He had published one volume of poems at his own expense, and another with a minor but respectable publishing house, and he went about giving readings to small literary groups. He was said to be "difficult," which meant that he considered himself an important poet and therefore in a different category from the ordinary professor. Considerations of rank and tenure were beneath his notice; he had other irons in his fire, and teaching classes was mainly a convenient way to support himself. I suppose I tend to be jealous of people like that—or of anyone so full of certainty about his cultural importance. But I suppose also that Merlin, like most such people, was using his arrogance as a hedge against inward fear—which doesn't make me like him any better.

Anyway, he was full of repressed anger. His thin mouth grew thinner. His pale skin seemed to turn yellow. But he spoke in low even tones. The main concern of the department seemed to be to turn out respectable and unimaginative statisticians. His business was poetry, and the first essential of poetry is the unfettered imagination. It is idiotic, he said, to profess poetry and pretend to admire it, and then to suppress the real thing when it appears. Mortimer Finkel may not be a respectable Eliot, but in his own uninhibited way he is a poet.

Willett looked at me. How did I feel about it?

What I felt was that they were both right, but you can't say that—not literally. The truth is that our whole academic operation rests on a paradox. The method of science is one thing, the method of art another. That may be obvious, but the difficulty is that we go on assuming that the two can be united. Mortimer Finkel the poet was supposed to get an A in Fulmar's graduate seminar in the Age of Johnson.

I mumbled something indecisive about giving him as much rope as possible, but I don't think they cared what I thought or said. They were too angry with each other to speak or listen, and Merlin stalked out abruptly.

"I wish the little son of a bitch would shave off that beard. He goes around looking like a pawnbroker's assistant." Willett meant Finkel, not Merlin, but his tone lumped them together.

But that's what happens in our department.

I should add that once, a long time ago, perhaps twenty-five years or more, my wife Harriet fell in love with Willett. She regarded herself as a brilliant and beautiful girl, and was full of expectations of passion and adventure. I can't say exactly what Willett's rôle in the affair was, but he has dealt with many women in his life and for all his chivalry he can, as men say, take care of himself.

But marriage and old loves make up a long story. I don't know that I can ever get into it.

CHAPTER 4

ROBERT SANDERLING is normal in appearance, inconspicuous, five feet ten and a half, a hundred and seventy pounds, active enough, though not rugged. Hair once brown, now gray and fairly thin, parted on the left and combed diagonally backward—often windblown. Skin reddish, easily burned, but weathered. Brown mole near left temple, also brown age markings appearing on backs of hands and elsewhere. . . .

All in all a recognizable *homo sapiens*.

For twenty years most of my physical energy has gone into the effort to control the size of my belly. I was never an athlete like Willett. My best sport as a youngster was pitching horseshoes, and even at that I was no champion. In college my efforts at tennis were somewhat laughable, though I never took them seriously enough to be troubled: a mistake, doubtless, since success of any sort calls for serious effort. I could run pretty well, and pictured myself winning mile races—I think I did make a serious effort to, but there were always three or four others who did better. When you fail at that sort of thing you consider it a moral failure, a deficiency of character, as I did for many years; you don't believe it is simply a matter of physical equipment. Once I came in third in an inter-class cross country run, a minor event in the college world, and the coach who gave out the awards told us that cross country running took more sheer guts than any other sport, and he congratulated us. Sheer guts—that's exactly what he said forty years ago. It's the kind of thing you remember.

But I walked a great deal, and still do. It is what an only son does. He is alone, without competition, and walking seems to be the way of least resistance. My father was a walker too, and on Sundays and other special days he took me on pre-planned circuits of five or six miles through the western suburbs—always with an eye for values in real estate, which was his business. When I was little the way often seemed long and weary, but somehow that is part of the pleasure of walking. Monotony, boredom, dust and heat— you go through a kind of ordeal and emerge thankfully. You feel better afterward.

From my house to the university is about five miles, and I do it in an hour and a half. Long ago I could keep up a pace of five miles an hour, which might be described as hard and serious walking. I can still do four miles an hour, and sometimes on cold days I do it as a demonstration to myself. I think a good deal about my belly, and I take note of other men to see how big their middles are. The human frame, I suppose, was never meant to stand upright, and the weak back and sagging belly are among our serious human handicaps. I can't say that I have won any sort of triumph over infirmity: for all my efforts my middle stays soft and a bit bulgy, and my back sometimes feels the knife thrusts of lumbago. I used to lift my legs up and down thirty times before I got out of bed in the morning, which I found very good for back and belly both, but Harriet was so persistent in her mockery that I tried to do it when she was not there to see—on the floor of my study before I went to bed at night, or even sometimes in my office at the university, though once our secretary walked in, thinking I had gone home, and found me with my legs in the air. A professor of my age can afford to be eccentric, of course—it is in fact expected of him by his public—but it is not well for him to act like a fool.

Some of my colleagues play squash, and a few meet at a club once a week to play tennis on an indoor court, but part of my folly in life is a self-consciousness about the conviviality of clubs. I do envy the ones who talk and drink and know the techniques of games, but I am not at home with them—as Willett is, for one. I can drink expertly enough, having learned the finer points over the years from Harriet—and perhaps our drinking is the one thing that has kept us together as man and wife. But of course I was brought up never to touch liquor and was well into my thirties before I tasted whisky—and I say "of course" because all old-fashioned New Englanders of my generation were brought up that way. Harriet was too, but she thought of herself as cosmopolitan and felt that good drinking habits should be part of her style. In the end the habits cut a lot deeper than that, as we both have found out. I tend to be very quiet and even secretive about it, as I am about everything, and the hearty locker-room and club-room sort of thing makes me feel inadequate. But it is fair to say that I have enough vanity about my health and figure and reputation to drink very moderately. Harriet drinks too much.

Instead of walking the long five miles homeward, I often head into the city the other way, nearly always with a little hopeful sense of escape and adventure. Once out of the university building and stepping briskly on the city walks I feel the release of perfect freedom. No questions, no duties or conflicts, nothing about me but pure impersonal triviality, store windows with bottles or electric drills, excavations for new buildings, moving cars, people. I have in mind errands, a second-hand bookstore, a picture gallery, bargain basement for a cheap pair of shoes with heavy rubber soles suitable for walking on endless pavements. I like to buy cheap things, but I realize my feet and ankles ache because of the bad shoes I wear; I keep looking for good shoes at bargain prices.

One of the illusions that keep a professor going is the sense of his importance. He is a learned man. He is observed in libraries delving into his material. His schedule is heavy. He sits on committees. He lectures. He exercises authority. He is clothed in learning and wisdom. He resents being bothered by trivialities, and is seen only by appointment. How much of it is justified by his life and work, how much is a charade, only his conscience knows. I have enjoyed the academic prerogatives for so long that I don't intend to turn against them, but as time goes on I realize that I am a good deal of an imposter. When I slip out of my office at three o'clock and head down town I know that I am being an idler and a waster of time. I pass within a block of the presidential mansion and I assume that it takes note of me with Gothic disapproval. I step along with a mind full of trifles. I watch the legs of girls and the blowing short skirts, and I search their faces for that vision that every man yearns for. I see a great clock high against the sky advertising a bottled drink. I have three free hours. I need not speak to anyone, answer questions, pretend to wisdom. I can stop for coffee at a counter, or a glass of ginger ale with ice cream in it, or a chocolate milkshake. I can buy a *New Yorker* or *Look*. I can stop at the galleries on Newbury Street, the new ones with Rorschach splashes, the old ones with snow and sea—I see a lot of pictures and have my favorites: in fact I am known to the attendants and proprietors, and they nod and smile to me. Sometimes I make up an errand at the great public library so that I can stroll through the portals and up the marble stairs, resuming a more professorial look as I head for the catalogue room. It is a good place to be seen, though I think my motive is mainly the pleasure of being in so fine a palace. I can sit for a long time waiting for a book with a sense of being suspended in a dream, surrounded by what always seem like quaint little human oddities coming and going, with the fateful romance of King Arthur in the dark murals on the walls. I look at those pictures and think of Harriet, my wife.

I nearly always stop at a big second-hand bookstore and then realize that there is no time to go on to the bargain basements farther down town. It will take me forty minutes to get home, and Harriet will have the martinis all iced on the dot of six. I am reluctant to spend money on anything, especially small amounts, so I don't buy many books, but I can browse endlessly. They leave me alone, the clerks—most of them know my habits by now, and they recognize me as a harmless and anonymous sort of person. Actually I don't own or read nearly enough books for a man of my position. You should see Grosbeck's library, for example—and any one of his articles gives you an annotated bibliography a yard long. Our university library is so crowded and frantic that I simply stay out of it. I don't "keep up," except as I browse in the bookstores and collect chance items.

This is all very minor stuff, of course, but if I have any validity as a professorial type there may be some excuse for recounting it. Other types exist too, obviously, and my hope is to let them be seen.

Home by six then. A long subway and surface ride, a last walk of three quarters of a mile. I do walk a good deal. I have learned to endure the subways and trolleys and busses with patience, and am actually an expert on their ways. The fact is that I don't like to drive a car. Harriet does, of course—and does so very well. People who drive cars hate to ride in what is called public transportation: they lose their freedom, somehow. They feel insignificant. But they all tell me I am lucky not to bother with a car, and they expatiate about traffic, parking, upkeep, and the endless troubles that follow. Harriet certainly spends a lot on the car, but she couldn't live without it.

Anyway, home by six, thirsty, ready for a drink. Legs a bit achy from the pavements, feet a bit swollen. I don't tell her where I have been—I leave briefcase and hat in the hall, go to the little downstairs toilet, wash hands, settle into a Danish arm chair just as Harriet pours the first drink. There is a plate of thin crackers.

"Here's how," she says in her vibrant throaty voice.

"Cheers," I say.

Her hair is still black. She may rub something into it, but I don't know. It is very fine hair and now looks rather queenly; it seems to be done up in a fine architectural mass. I see her face as fine and beautiful too, though I realize that I still see it as it was twenty-six or eight years ago. She used to wear her hair in a braided crown then, but she always looked like a medieval queen, or like the legendary Morgana. That's why the murals in the Library made me think of her. It was too strong a face for what passes popularly as beauty, but such words as regal and fateful come to mind as one remembers her. Now I fear she has become just another woman ravaged by age, with harsh lines of disappointment and discontent. I realize that, but of course I can see the lost beauty and youth in her too.

It is obvious that Harriet occupies a large place in my life. Yet in actuality we follow separate ways. We live in the same house, and for a good many years we slept in the same bed; we go out to dinner or to departmental parties together— where I must confess she seems to take most pleasure in telling about my follies and absurdities. She can be very funny on the subject. I suppose an observer would say that at such times I hate her, but I find it hard to explain just how I do feel. She is formidable, not only as a personality at a party but as a whole lifetime character; she seems to me actually more intelligent, more gifted, more potential, than anyone I have known.

But during the ordinary days we hardly meet until the six o'clock drink. I am the kind who gets up early and goes to bed early (she is the opposite), and I get my breakfast, read the morning paper, and go about my day's affairs before she stirs—and normally I have morning classes to meet. She is not a lazy woman though, or self-indulgent in the familiar ways of the female. We live in what everyone considers a charming house, and almost every bit of its charm is a result of her planning, and some of it of her labor. She paints, papers, upholsters, hammers, saws. She creates pictures for the walls, and rugs and drapes, and even carved and modelled figures for tables or mantels—and has lately gone in for the abstractions of modernism. I never know what she may be up to, and she never explains herself or consults me, but of course she delights in the praises and triumphs of accomplishment. But she is never content: she hangs a four-foot oil painting above the fire place, looks at it for a week with increasing disapproval, then destroys it. She picks up a clay figurine, studies it with the glittery sneer so characteristic of her, and tosses it on the bricks of the hearth. "The hell with that thing," she says buoyantly, as though she had done something dramatic and clever. She saves her more histrionic acts for an audience—for a dinner party, say, where she sometimes speaks blasphemies.

I suppose her dream was always of herself as an actress. She did well in college dramatics, and remembers herself as Medea and Antigone and Goneril. "Don't you think I was born to be Goneril? An absolute five-star bitch—I could play her for all she was worth." But of course she didn't really think of herself as a five-star bitch. Her true vision of herself was as Candida, the wise and dominant female who assumed that all men were little boys who leaned on her for comfort and flattery—and in a local performance some years ago she won great acclaim in the rôle. Her last big part was Mistress Quickly—and since then she has been a witch in *Macbeth*. "My destiny," she says.

At different times in the past she has played more conventional rôles in the League of Women Voters and the Garden Club, but I think her chief desire is to administer needlepricks of shock to all those good earnest women, as she calls them. "I get the urge to throw coffee cups," she says. "Some day I'll just cut loose, I'll rip up their whole damned peapatch."

As I said, she has a resonant throaty voice, with sardonic overtones, and nearly everything she says is meant to be ironic or funny. People are vividly aware of her, and her presence quickens any gathering, but she has almost no friends—only one, I'd say, Evelyn Piper, the spinster daughter of old John who prematurely retired ten years ago. And I realize as I say it how little she now has to do with ordinary life. I have talked of her acting and her other doings, but they are mostly so much in the past that they don't count any more. Perhaps the witch's part finished her. Evelyn is a conventional woman, but the two make a little unit together—and Harriet can dominate and control.

There's Joan too. Gone now, after strong declarations and ultimatums: we don't speak of her, not even when I go and visit her in summer. It is strange to live with such silences and evasions, and I feel to blame—whether Harriet does I can't say but she wouldn't admit it under torture. She likes to publish the fact that she is a bitch, and that she enjoys being a bitch, but she sees it as a heroic rôle, she sees her embattled self standing against the cowards and hypocrites that surround her. But I have never known her to accept blame for any failure or error. It was always Joan's fault—*she* was the stubborn one, the ungrateful self-seeker.

Joan was intended to be a junior partner. She would play the rôle that Harriet always dreamed of playing. She would be beautiful and brilliant and talented, she would exist above the commonplace levels, she would obey only the dictates of her own free nature. But the basic training was intensive and in the end self-defeating. She didn't have to be a professional, Harriet said. Professionalism itself leads to a commercial conformity. But she must know the techniques, the language, the notes, the steps. She must achieve absolute poise in any situation. If called upon to sing, or dance, or recite, or act, she must do it with uninhibited grace. And she must be beautifully herself—or even fiercely herself, because Harriet conceived of self-hood as a hard-won battle. If in the end she had great talent she would rise with it into a life of splendid fulfilment.

That has been Harriet's dream, and I think I state it fairly. For her, and for Joan, it has led to disappointment and unhappiness, but the dream itself is universal and forever beguiling and it may achieve the glory it hopes for. I am not one who denies human glory, or even happiness, as it seems fashionable to do. But I have lived through the travail of wife and daughter—I suppose I have shared a good deal of it and still do. At the worst of it, eight or nine years ago, I developed a case of stomach ulcers, which are the marks of inward griefs or pressures.

Joan represents a wholly different temperament, in its own way as intractable as Harriet's. I suppose plain is one word for it, but other words do better: basic, earthy, practical. Stubborn too, with a tough inward strength that was developed by years of silent battling against Harriet's flamboyance. Joan listens a lot, says little, and takes no one's word for anything without first passing it through rigid inspection. But her main feature is plainness, which is what offends Harriet more than anything. "She doesn't *have* to look like a mule—she doesn't have to act like one either . . . ." The biggest uproar occurred when Joan was sixteen and began to fight against all the art and music and dramatics and said she intended to be a veterinarian. She collected creatures of all kinds, mice, rats, guinea pigs, snakes, lizards—and right now is trying to raise chinchillas near Port Jervis, New York, where her husband teaches school.

We don't speak of Joan at all. It is a strange kind of tension. Joan herself doesn't nourish hatred. She is wholly intent on her affairs and family, and as everyone says of her is "a hard worker," but in her cards and notes and recognitions she includes Harriet in a routine sort of way. But from Harriet's point of view the affair is a drama that must be acted out in classic style. She doesn't say "how sharper than a serpent's tooth," because she considers the lines too much of a cliché, but that is pretty much her conception of the issue.

So we have martinis, and she says "Here's how," and I say "Cheers."

The house is very pleasant to be in, though it is so wholly hers that I never feel quite responsible for it—except in two places: my study, of course, which is upstairs, and a stretch of grassy yard behind the garage and by chance isolated from the rest of the place. Over the years Harriet has arranged and planned things with devotion and hope. She is neither a good housekeeper nor a good gardener, and whatever she does is done with free-hand speed—often very effectively; but she insists on hiring a once-a-week man for outside work, and a twice-a-week woman for cleaning and washing. The expense is very great. She does cook the dinner—with speed and flair, and is pleased to be imaginative and somewhat extravagant. We seldom have common meat and potatoes and boiled vegetables, but rather casseroles and sauces and salads; we go through cycles of Italian or Chinese or Mexican experiment.

"I know you would live on hamburgers and boiled carrots if you could," she says. "And *tea*." She always scorns tea, and uses it as a symbol of all that is flat and conventional. The collapse of the British Empire, she says, is an obvious result of their addiction to tea and boiled potatoes. Food like theirs is enough to destroy any civilization. But then, French food in its way is just as bad because they are insane about it. French recipes infuriate her, and she walks up and down our living room reading them aloud in theatrical tones. "Simmer three hours and *reserve liquid*. Cream one cup of unsalted butter—" She makes it sound Shakespearean. "They can all just go to hell with their three hours of simmering and their pounds of butter."

She is good at spaghetti sauce, though, and this evening we may have it, and a lettuce salad with herbs, and a bottle of Chianti. What with the martinis and the wine we get a little blurry, and I for one feel more like a nap than anything else. She equates naps with tea and hamburgers, and goes off alone to a movie, which she makes a habit of doing.

✑ CHAPTER 5 ❧

In the Newton area west of Boston, where we live, there are few really good houses. A New Englander's idea of a "good" house is one built with architectural distinction before or soon after the year 1800, and in some of our towns there are a great many. But Newton seems to have been a pleasant country district until nearly 1900, when it was translated into a Boston suburb. The few old houses were submerged in a flood of shingles and stucco and machine-made Georgian— and now in these later times with ranches and split-levels and prefabrications. Some of the new ones are of course admirable in their own fashion, and some are elegant and some charming, but the general run of Newton architecture has no character at all. It is what Harriet calls a middle-class mess.

We lived for a time in a chocolate-colored bungalow that illustrated the taste of 1907, a very snug, cavelike place where sun and even daylight hardly penetrated. Harriet refers to our first year there as the Idyll of the Cave, and is very pleased with her wit. She made herself miserable with a succession of frustrations and defeats, and would have gone back to

58

mother (as she often said) except that she couldn't stand her mother—or any of the rest of her family. She said such things with sardonic triumph, as though the truth would astonish and delight her hearers—and the question is always how to take it: or perhaps how to take her. As I have remarked, she is a very magnetic woman, in spite of what she says and does.

But it was the new house that saved us—that and George Willett, perhaps. If you assume that I am a complaisant husband, or even a cuckold in the old tradition, you may be right, but I can't believe that the labels have much relevance. Anyone who thinks he can deal with such a woman in conventional fashion is being naïve. I've never been able to talk to Willett about it, he being very much of a varsity gentleman, but I'd like to overhear his version of the affair. He doesn't know that I know anything about it.

Anyway—the house. She found it. A dismal little gray clapboard box in an alley called Lafayette Place. At that time business was bad, people were poor, and houses stood empty, but to Harriet it was a major opportunity. She turned into a woman of executive energy, and bargained and haggled and consulted builders and bankers and lawyers. I told her we didn't have money enough, but she went on with it as though her destiny required it, and I admired and loved her. She swept all before her.

The house had been built in 1821—we found the date on a rafter. It had the lines of a slightly crooked packing crate with a peaked slate roof, with no frills anywhere. But like all houses of that era it had a mysterious kind of appeal. You glanced at it twice. Its shape was right. The clapboards were more charming than modern clapboards. You could see that it was a poor relation to a "good" house. Doubtless a caretaker or resident farmer had lived in it a century ago. And behind it lay a tangled half acre with a couple of forgotten apple trees in it.

I used to be able to handle small business affairs. After all, my father was a real estate man, and his people were mostly in business of one sort or another; I'm not the kind of literary character who scorns the practical. But Harriet took over. She acted like one obsessed. She glittered with the excitement of it. It got so I simply signed documents where she indicated. It is the one time in her life when she brought all her passions and energies to bear on a single big operation.

Perhaps as the world looks at things, these events are small indeed; but to me Harriet has all the makings of a great woman, a Catherine of Russia, say, or a Margaret of Anjou, and this was at least a start in the direction of fulfilment. The men she hired were always delighted and flattered to work for her, and made her a temporary partner in their trade. She sat on boxes and talked in wise-cracks with plumbers. She climbed ladders and perched on eaves to see how the new chimney was coming along. She designed and drew to scale doorways and mantels, and the carpenter took her home to meet his wife and children. She scoured the region for material, and was a ruthless bargainer for second-hand bricks or flagstones or brass pipes. She removed a century of old wallpaper, and scraped and sanded and painted woodwork. She salvaged a white picket fence, with gates, and had it set up in front, and it looked as though it had been there forever. Her special pride was the treatment of the front doorway, which she transformed from a rectangular hole in the wall to a classic Georgian order, with cornice, slim pilasters, and little side-light windows.

So in the course of a summer we moved ourselves from the

sunless cave of the bungalow to a serene and pleasant little model of New England classic. I accepted everything she did; I had no say in any of her arrangements, and was delighted to have a study for myself upstairs with bookshelves on all the walls, windows facing west and south, and a couch. Our mood was buoyant then. I was happy that she was happy. I admired her skill and nerve. I listened to her plans. "I don't give a damn about antiques as such," she said. "All I want is something that looks right. Is that sideboard authentic or isn't it? It looks fine, doesn't it? I got it for eight bucks in a junk-place in Watertown—"

"Doubtless they wanted ten for it."

"They expected ten. It was marked twelve."

In these times of prosperous inflation it is hard to believe that things were once so cheap. She got the property itself for four thousand, and put another four thousand into it—and that was almost more than we could manage on my little salary. But she arranged very good mortgage terms. Professors were supposed to be trustworthy, at least.

And what pleasure she took in the general praise and astonishment of colleagues and friends. Some had seen it as it originally was, and could not have believed it possible. For a while we were on show, and for all her cynicism Harriet basked in the success of our enterprise. The half acre was translated into lawns and flowers—never very formal or even neat, since her style was always slapdash, but somehow imaginative and characteristic of her, with little paths among the half-wild forsythia and lilacs. The white fence, white clapboards, dark-green shutters, classic doorway, give such a style to the neighborhood that what was once a neglected alley is now a desirable location, as real estate people say, and I think there are those who refer to Harriet as the Marquise—

in honor of our distinguished name, Lafayette Place.

And after all that, she said she wanted a baby. She had almost no maternal desires, but there was the pretty house with a small extra bedroom. Her temperament is strongly artistic, as I have said; she is always creating things, pictures, statuary, settings, even acts, and the vision of a child appropriately dwelling in her house was irresistible. It's no good just for us, she said. Who are *we*, anyway? A couple of sterile nonentities. Why do we rate a nice house just for ourselves . . . .

She had certainly not grown up with the idea that she was a nonentity, or sterile, but her habit was to speak sardonically about everything, including herself. The words were meant more seriously as an attack on me.

She had consistently needled me for being a nonentity. At times of anger, which used to be frequent, she has attacked me for every possible inadequacy. They made me a professor because they were stuck with me. They put me on this or that committee because they know I'll do the dirty work, but if anything important comes up I'm the last one they consult. My salary is way below what they announce as the scale. I'm the kind of nice guy who always finishes last . . . . She can say these things as though they were jests, with sharp ironic edges, and of course I have to admit that she is mostly right. The jests are effective. We say the same sort of thing about other people all the time—not in their hearing: but would it be reasonable of me to note that since I am trained to accept truth as it appears in literature, I am at least trying to accept it in life also? Much of what Harriet says is recognizably true, though I am not naïve enough to take it as the whole truth. But as long as I can remain detached I can agree with her. She has always wanted celebrity, not because she is avaricious or childish about fame or luxury, but because she thinks of herself as the equal of anyone anywhere: she knows she could handle any president or king or dictator—she could, if she ever got a chance, be an immortal historical character. That's part of her dream, at least. And she is stuck in a little suburban dead-end with an unheard-of professor named Robert Sanderling.

I realize that many will condemn her for one thing, and me for another, but the truth about human affairs is interesting for its own sake: what people accept with approval or disapproval is often only the stereotyped assumption they take for granted. Harriet is not a psychological cliché. As for Sanderling, he doesn't think big, as his colleague told him after three drinks.

But the question of sterility is a biological one. The belief that all success and failure in life is at bottom sexual is so strong in our century that in serious art, at least, no other view is allowed. And I am obviously not equipped to deal with it in the expected clinical fashion—in origin and early experience I belong to an older era. But I can hint at what must be obvious to all. We didn't get along well, and she accused me of impotence and unworthiness. The fact is that in those early days in the bungalow she positively repelled me—she scared me. It wasn't exactly ferocity and crudeness. Her washing and dressing habits were irregular—in fact sloppy. She took a sardonic view of all the rituals of lovemaking and often began to abuse me before we had fairly got started on the business. I knew I wasn't impotent, because I had already been in love and had had hasty and rather desperate relations with a girl when I was in graduate school—an affair that filled me with ecstasy and bewilderment and shame.

It would sound as though Harriet married me in a spirit of

contempt—and perhaps she did. She had been engaged to two or three other men, or at least had seriously considered marrying them: the last one was an actor who later became well known, and she fully intended and expected to marry him. She spoke of him afterward with eager hatred—always as That Bastard—and watched his career closely. It was the time when I had written the novel, and was circulating a little bit among the literary folk. What girls I had had up to then had been shy and pale and scared—kindred spirits, perhaps. Thirty years ago the suburban world was full of what all parents spoke of as *nice* girls, who lived wholly in a sort of cotton-wool nest of propriety and innocence. Perhaps no female is really innocent; it is not in their nature to be, and most are of course deadly in their instinctual operations. But the young girls of that era were perfect in their propriety, and many lived in fear.

But Harriet—Harriet Earnshaw as she was then—behaved with deliberate emancipation. She bobbed her hair. She painted her lips. She wore short skirts—and sometimes trousers. She spoke out freely and profanely. She had to do with the theatre, was seen with actors. The reputation of the nineteen-twenties for wildness is absurdly exaggerated by later journalists, but at least the beginnings of the moral anarchy of our world occurred then. And Harriet, who had left home in a rage of revolt, was doing her best to shock the middle-class puritans she had been brought up with.

It must be realized that underneath the glittery external armor there is nearly always a vulnerable hide and heart, and I suppose Harriet took to me out of sheer human weakness. It was easy for her. She was bright and beautiful, and she seemed to know everything: she dazzled me. But she had actually had no success with the men she wanted. I suppose she scared them off. She began to believe that she was being rejected and left behind, though I doubt if she would ever admit it—not in such banal terms, at least; but I see many girls going through similar affairs, and some confide in me. There comes a time when almost any man is better than none. I naturally advise patience and philosophical detachment.

So our union was awkward on both sides, and we lived in the chocolate bungalow in a fashion that would be considered deplorable by the sexual scientists. One of us was always sleeping on the couch in the study. I should add that my elderly mother occupied the other bedroom upstairs, and thereby doubled our tensions: a kind, good, simple-hearted woman who made no demands, expressed few opinions, dusted the house, washed most of the dishes, yet whose presence seemed to make for explosive frustrations. My mother was inclined to be sentimental in the sad half-tearful way of the old days, and when she lost her vocation as active wife and mother she began to dwindle away, she failed, as they used to say, and she died before we ever moved to Lafayette Place. Harriet's stated policy was always to be "good to her," and she tried as best she could, but she couldn't resist the habit of needling me for the futile sentimentalities she implied I shared with my mother.

I'm sure my mother had no inkling of the absurd sexual antics that went on, the quarrels and frustrations and accusations and reconciliations, the sleepings on the couch, the bedroom contests at odd hours of the day, the times of mortal enmity—she lived in a little dream of her own, was sweet and polite through every crisis. She wasn't happy, I fear; she cried in secret—but not really because of us, rather because of age and loss.

Harriet at first had no desire for a child, and was fearful of being pregnant, but after a while she decided we weren't in much danger, as she put it. In the two years of the chocolate bungalow we did manage some sexual unions. After a few months in Lafayette Place she cheerily announced herself as pregnant, and went through with the bearing of Joan with great good will.

It may seem remarkable that we stuck together. If it hadn't been for the new house and the baby we would certainly have broken up, but that doesn't really explain why we lasted through the early bungalow period and through later years. It seems to be expected that marriages fail in these times.

I suppose I have a deep-rooted respect and devotion for Harriet. Her beauty seemed splendid to me, and I was always filled with pride and surprise at having her for a wife; but more than that she has had what amounts to a controlling power over me, and when I compare her with reigning queens I am partly serious in seeing a genius for domination in her. Her judgments are decisive and her mind jumps to quick and bold solutions, whereas I am always half-lost in the blurry middle ground. Such philosophy as I have tells me that though extreme positions are often effective and may be justified by some temporary necessity, they are at bottom unwise. In other words, I am a born compromiser. From the simplest to the most complicated of choices I find it nearly impossible to be decisive and final. Harriet assumes that she is appointed to do my thinking for me, and orders meals and clothes and other daily essentials with no hesitation.

I must say it sounds as though I were no better than a tame rabbit in the clutches of a conjuror, but in actuality I see myself as operating with more real freedom than most men are allowed in their lives. My mind is free: it may in truth be half-lost in its middle ground of compromise, but such as it is that is my territory and that is where for better or worse I am fated to live. And I carry on my profession with as much freedom as is given to any man in organized society—that too is a truth to be noted. But the sexual scientists would only be preoccupied with my failures and frustrations, and I suppose if a novelist were to bother with me at all he would make me into a figure of ignominy and futility. I fear them, these arrogant critics of *homo sapiens* who gloat on failure and make their living out of it, but I can only attest that in spite of all the recognized and coded human weaknesses I have got along pretty well.

The larger question is why Harriet has stuck to me. After her early dreams of some sort of personal grandeur she has suffered disappointment. Hers is certainly the "failure" that critics of humanity are always mentioning. And her daily attitude seems to recognize it, her needling of me, her references to sterility and impotence (still part of her jesting vocabulary), her implication that she is trapped.

But she is more complicated than most people, as I have said. She can, for example, act with calculation and policy—and I suppose that is what she has been doing since the beginning. With all her dreams and frustrations she accepts the realities and makes use of them, and among the essentials she has agreed with herself to accept are her house and her husband. Joan said of her once that she had no heart, which is the sort of thing you say in the midst of a quarrel. Harriet might even say it of herself in a moment of bitter candor. She obviously scorns sentiment. She mocks good intentions. But in time of trouble, emergency, death, disaster, she acts with selfless devotion. I think she could have arranged for my death on one or two occasions of major illness, and I am sure she was aware of the possibility and rationally considered it: if murder were part of her policy she would not hold back. But she has always taken conscientious care of me, sometimes with heroic fortitude and loyalty.

I had a severe infection of the kidneys just after we moved to Lafayette Place, and spent days in the hospital, but for a month afterward I was weak and miserable. She took charge of me with enormous buoyancy. She had just created her house, and was excited by the adventure and triumph of it. She was seeing Willett, and the excitement of that was even greater. And she was attending to my needs with wonderful competence. It was as though she had come out into full sunlight for the first time. She glowed, her voice deepened, she stood straighter—many people remarked on her beauty. She let her hair grow longer and wove it into a queenly crown.

◄ৡ CHAPTER 6 ৡ►

WE USED TO GIVE an annual party for the department. Harriet arranged the drinks and food; I distributed the invitations.

"I like to see them with their guard down," she said.

It's true. She likes to drink and she likes to see other people drink. She can hold it well, as they say, but she grows edgier and more sardonic, and sometimes her candor is embarrassing. Her perceptions are sharper. Mine on the contrary grow duller, and all I want to do after three drinks is to lie down.

The wives came too, and some of the secretaries and assistants, and after the last one a couple of years ago we gave up. The house was jammed full, everyone stood up chest to chest and shouted, the rugs and furniture suffered, and we all seemed to be smothered in noise and numbers.

"It's not worth it," I said to Harriet afterward.

"Oh, I don't know. They thought it was. They love free drinks."

It is a fact, I suppose, that people will go to great lengths for free drinks. It sounds cynical as she put it. But I think the drinking together is the important part, that and the sense each individual has of risk and adventure. The supply of liquor is unlimited, of course—it is up to the host to urge it upon his guests without cease, and everyone must decide how far to go with it. Quick calculations must be made, as whether one drives or is driven, or whether trouble will follow at home, or the miseries of a hangover, or even loss of face, as the Asians put it. The risk itself is stimulating. But more than the challenge of alcohol is the excitement of being together, of standing chest to chest and shouting and laughing. In their ordinary encounters, college teachers eye one another warily—not with hostility, unless there are unusual personal frictions, but often with jealous admiration and undeclared rivalry; but at a party with drinks their guard, as Harriet said, does come down. They make joyful noises. They shout across the room. They eye wives with curiosity and pleasure. Even the few who don't drink are swept along on the floods of noise and good cheer. We ought to do this more, they say. We don't see enough of each other—we don't really get together . . . .

Later, on sober thought, they may deny any pleasure in the event. These parties, they say, these damned parties—you can't talk to anyone, you can't even sit down; you just push your way in and stand. It is a kind of primitive ritual. What we ought to have really is a colloquium of some sort, where you could expect some intelligent talk.

That is always the dream of the academic person: the brilliant colloquium in which "discussion" reaches a high level of eloquence and wit.

But probably the best of our parties are the ones given by the Medricks—at least they used to be thought of as the major social event of the academic year. But since the last one exploded into a brawl, as everyone later described it, the Medricks may give up too. They live in a big house just off Brattle Street in Cambridge, and are part of the aristocracy of that neighborhood. I really don't know what his family origins are: his degrees are from Chicago and Oxford, and he has the polished voice and accent of an English actor. In rainy weather he wears a cape, and the brim of his hat is broader than normal—he also carries an umbrella, seldom unrolled. You know he is a gentleman, of course. He has a smartly trimmed little beard, a pointed horizontal mustache, and a wavy sweep of white hair. A grandee, in fact. I think everyone likes him, and everyone assumes that as a scholar he is nothing but a magnificent bluff. But in our business that kind of magnificence is still very successful, though it is getting to be rare. Medrick rates as an unforgettable character, an aristocrat of letters, a Chesterfieldian gentleman, and his students never forget him. The Duke, they call him, and tell old tales of his wit and manner. "If you will bear with me," he says at the close of a lecture as bells begin to ring, "I have a few last pearls . . . ."

The Old Pretender, McLoon calls him.

The world of Brattle Street, with house and money, belongs to Avis Medrick, whose father lived there during his tenure as dean of the Harvard Law School and later Judge of the state Supreme Court. The house is still designated as Judge Crary's, and everyone who knows the Medricks is aware that she is Judge Crary's daughter, though it is never she who in any way alludes to it. She is actually bowed down with anxious modesty. I suppose her clothes are the best, but she seems always to be loosely tied together with scraps and streamers. In any small crisis she breathes and snuffles and perspires. She wears the kind of fragile eye-glasses that balance temporarily on the nose, and she has the habit of tipping her head back to hold them there.

I don't know that anyone really ever loved her in the course of her life: her only child was mentally defective, and long since dead. But many people liked her. The emotion was always tinged with sorrow: poor Avis, she means so well, she is really so *nice*, she'd do anything for you. She strove for good, she worked in the ranks for causes—women's suffrage years ago as a young girl, and then unmarried mothers, and slum welfare, and birth control, and saving shade trees. She keeps liberal publications on her library table, goes to lectures and meetings, is recognized at State House hearings, and plays perfectly the part of the absurd gentlewoman full of futile good intentions. "But I never can *speak*," she says. "I do so wish I had had courage enough to take *lessons*, like Mrs. Roosevelt." Her voice tends to break into soprano wails and laughs, as though she were being specially charming and funny. "I should have done it years ago. I could never even recite in *school*." The little wail and laugh imply that her predicament must seem very ridiculous to all sensible people.

"That's the girl you ought to have married," Harriet said once. "Plenty of money and good intentions." She said such things with relish. She thought Avis Medrick was the same kind of a fool as I was, and in a way I had to agree with her. I liked Avis and felt at home with her. Not that I ever went in for causes, except for the Sunday School work I used to do at our Church—and I've been in the men's club there for forty years or so—but Avis and her good intentions seemed very understandable to me.

Her parties represented a clear duty to her. She had a big

house. She supplied the best liquor. Her husband was manifestly the number one man in our department, and though we were not Harvard, which she had been brought up to consider the cultural standard of the world, we were her responsibility. Horace, she said, had the greatest admiration for the work we did. Horace believed particularly in our future.

Horace seemed born to be a host in the grand manner. It would be easy to see him as a classic charlatan, with his English suits and his vandyke and the noble sweep of white hair above his scholar's brow, but as I said, we all like him. We assume that he has married for money, and his professorship has come as a recognition of his social and histrionic talents, and a few of us are brutally candid about his pretensions to scholarship, but we take pleasure in his flair. Our academic self-importance gets to be pretty dreary: the new school of university men produces bibliographical experts but few platform personalities. Undergraduates, at least, are always eager to admire a semi-legendary figure—old Prof. Medrick, the Duke himself, reading *The Tempest*, reading *Paradise Lost*: they never forget, and remind each other at reunions. To us who know him well, though, he is a most pleasant colleague. He does his duties without complaint, sits on committees, comes to meetings, is full of good cheer and amusing anecdotes. He is shrewd enough to assess his own status with us, and reminds us in one way or another that he makes every effort to pull his weight. He takes charge of the general introductory courses for sophomores and gives lectures in our biggest auditorium: his presentation of Shakespeare is greatly admired, and given special notice in the university bulletin.

What he particularly has is dignity, and I often remember how Sterne defined it in *Tristram Shandy*: a certain carriage of the body designed to conceal the defects of the mind. The way his head poises itself above his shoulders—I see him in his hall at our party, the princely host in quiet and beautiful tweed, placed under the light so that his hair and brow make a brightness of their own. Sterne wasn't fair, of course. Medrick's dignity is something he can't really help. Some men, no matter what they say, sound like embodied wisdom, and he is such a man. "My noble and approved good masters," he said with Shakespearean humor, "thrice welcome. Do come in and refresh yourselves. Avis, here are Harriet and Robert Sanderling—and you know—er—Mark Jaeger of course." That little hesitation, a clearing of throat, characteristically implied many things—a concession to first names, a kindly overture to the arrogant Jaeger, a chuckle at the charade he was part of. Medrick was always a master of the intermediate noises of speech.

The early phase of such a party can be cold and awkward. The first-comers sit down and try to make suitable conversation. Then the drink takes effect, more people come, everyone stands, talk is louder and more spontaneous—and in a big house full of big furniture, with high ceilings and oil paintings and oriental rugs, the pleasure becomes manifest. The younger men and their wives have a glimpse of cultural felicity and old-fashioned grandeur and they speak with more careful articulation and as much urbanity as they can muster—they have come from diapers and baby-sitters three flights up, their appointments are precarious, their future insecure, but here for an hour or two they see themselves as members of an aristocracy.

"Somewhat tarnished," young Dunlin noted as he looked at drapes and rugs. "Reminds one of the early Roxy period of silent movies."

I pointed out that he was too young to talk like that and

he smiled with self-approval. "Oh, I know my periods. General Grant, early Fall River Line, David Belasco—" He sipped his Scotch and looked at it. Young people know all about Scotch these days—all about everything. "This has cachet, though. A library with real books. Sargent water colors—they tell me the little girl with the parasol is Avis herself. And that could be a Winslow Homer between the windows. Don't you think we could invent a new period—late Brattle Street, say, or even mid-President Eliot?"

I note these remarks because our younger men do talk that way. They know what's what, are cynical, unsurprised, but interested, and more appreciative than they pretend. Anyone doing work on the Ticknor and Fields publishing operations had better come here, Dunlin said. Had I noticed the extraordinary collection of their books? I assured him that the Medricks would welcome him or any scholar, and he looked at me with a raised eyebrow as though the idea were quite preposterous. He himself had done his work (I use the standard locution for it) in Faulkner, and presumably considered Ticknor and Fields somewhat quaint.

We were standing partly in the large doorway between the main hall and one of the front rooms—a formal reception room, or perhaps music room since there was a grand piano in one corner. Because of the general spaciousness we weren't all massed together in the usual cocktail party fashion, and could move about and take observations. We saw the Grosbecks come in, followed by the McLoons, and Avis Medrick invited the ladies to leave their things upstairs. The two men stood for a moment glaring at each other with an odd sort of fixity until Medrick swept them along toward his big study where they were to leave coats and hats.

"I don't know how he holds together," Dunlin said.

"Who?"

"Why, Mac. He nourishes himself on Scotch."

It was somewhat later that McLoon remarked on my shortcomings. He couldn't rouse my anger, not then at least, because I was full of sorrow at the sight of him. It was evident that nature intended him to be a powerful and formidable man. He was taller than the rest of us, with broad sloping shoulders and long arms—his sinewy wrists thrust themselves out of his sleeves: he moved in angles and jerks, and seemed unsteady in his balance—not necessarily because of drink but because he had a bony, awkward, stiff-jointed body. I remember seeing him play tennis years ago, charging about like Don Q among the windmills, but so grim and determined that he scored points against all odds. Yet he did drink, and spent his latter days in a blur of alcoholic vapor. We were of course all afraid of him. His great gaunt face loomed over us like a disaster. He spoke out in meetings—he called Merlin the poet a pretentious bastard, and he called Willett an ivy-league poseur, and he called the rest of us mountebanks or pansies or intellectual pipsqueaks or whatever he thought appropriate. He was on the edge of madness, I suppose. Like the Old Testament king, he swore vengeance against all the world. But I can't explain why—unless it is simply a matter of alcohol. He was a scholar of power and promise, and his book of thirty years ago on Swift is still the best in its field. He has done nothing since then. He married a girl of an eminent family, and she has stuck with him through everything, but she is cold and somehow unapproachable, and many hold her to blame for his spiritual miseries. "Living with that woman," they say with emphasis.

A dour old-time Scot with no faith and no hope. To his students a Character, an oracular cynic who knows everything and respects nothing. Few speak in his classes or call attention to themselves, but they listen with close concern as he documents the stupidity and folly of mankind. This Ship of Fools, he says, this race of passionate, self-seeking, superstitious idiots all breeding like flies—but he says it with cold and bitter logic. I have no religious superstitions, he says, but I have an awareness of what justice means, and if those bombs destroy us I can only say that we deserve it—we have it coming to us. Civilization is just a way of being successfully predatory, it gives more and more scope to selfishness.

"You know what Grosbeck is?" he said to me at the party. "He's a damned German Fascist. He's one of those John Birchers."

I said I shouldn't have thought so. I assumed he was more than normally drunk, and I wasn't arguing with him.

"Those articles of his, all that scholarship—it's nothing but the old German kultur machine grinding along. What the hell good does any of it do? All he is is one of those Herr Doktor Professors who think they are the top crust of the master race. You know what he said? I heard him say it—just now. We'll have to use the bomb on them some day—better too early than too late. Use it on *them*, he said. That's the talk. Us good guys. Those bastards. Blow them into oblivion."

I did no more than make a few futile noises in reply. He expected no intelligent response from anyone, and I knew if I offered one of my inevitable clichés it would only deepen his contempt. Some of our young warriors had the nerve to make fun of him—Dunlin, for one, tried to goad him into more extravagant misanthropy; but it was dangerous sport. Better be an honest misanthrope, he said, than a smart-alec sophist, which is what the bright boys like Dunlin mostly were. Truth to them was simply a matter of scoring points. The bomb was useful for wise-cracks. As for Grosbeck—

"No wise-cracks there," I agreed too hastily. "He is surely very serious—very literal, perhaps." I spoke in a mumble because I didn't intend to distract him, and I assumed he would pay no attention. But of course he snapped it up. "Literal! You think that excuses him? God preserve us from serious people, specially German ones." McLoon seemed to lean over me like a colossus of despair. "*Exterminate the brutes*—that's what they really want. You know it as well as I do, Sanderling."

In a way I did know it, but I wouldn't admit it to McLoon. We all read *Heart of Darkness*, teach it in innumerable classes—some of us take it very seriously and literally. The scholar, the philosopher, the idealist, comes in the end under pressure to savagery. It happens. The wrong is done and millions of helpless people suffer. But what can a diffident and somewhat cowardly man do about it? March with placards? Speak? Write letters to the papers? Join a group? Proclaim that man is a savage creature and ought to be ashamed of himself?

McLoon takes to drink and utters anathemas.

He turned and raised his tinkling glass of Scotch and called in the voice of a prophet: "*Exterminate the brutes!*" He drank down the Scotch in dour and solemn silence, and seemed quite oblivious to the astonishment round him. Mrs. Medrick essayed a snuffly little social laugh.

Nothing might have come of it if he hadn't caught sight of Grosbeck walking in from the hall. He raised a long arm with a great bony finger at the end. "Mister Kurtz," he said in his harshest voice. "You'll join me. A glass for Mister Adolph Kurtz." He was of course drunker than anyone realized, but he spoke out with power.

Grosbeck looked from side to side to see what was going on. He was a chunky man with thick glasses and a habit of glancing quickly all about him as though he feared ambush. He realized that McLoon was on a rampage, and he caught the allusion to Mister Kurtz—in fact he probably took it all in at once: he had a very quick mind, along with a wary and defensive manner. Normally he had a powerfully rational approach to all problems and was so formidable in his judgments that no one ventured to dispute with him. But we knew there was something burning inside him. He wrote letters to the paper denouncing the morals and manners of our time. He deplored tobacco and drink and sex.

"Salvation by authority," McLoon went on, speaking clearly. "Be good, do right—or else. The *Herrenvolk* know best. Isn't that how it is, professor?"

"May I remind you, McLoon," Grosbeck said in his resonant lecturer's voice, "that my name has been native in Missouri for a hundred and fifteen years. If you dislike it because its origin is German, then I can only conclude that you are a cultural idiot—or that you are drunk, which is more likely."

The accent of disgust on the word "drunk" rang out as though it had been uttered on a stage.

Actually neither man had what is called a sense of humor. I can remember McLoon being cheerful long ago, and humor is made up of wit and good cheer—but he had lost his cheer, and his wit had corroded into despair. Grosbeck, of course, had no time for play of any sort. He was one of those relentless workers who produce learned article after learned article and then every second year or so compile them into a book—and it always seems incongruous to me that his major "field" is romanticism. It is characteristic of our profession that a scholar with no humor, no imagination, no poetic sensibility, should specialize in the age of Byron and Keats, and should be recognized all over the western world as an authority. Grosbeck is our most celebrated colleague.

McLoon, on his part, was almost impervious to insult. He agreed with the worst that could be said about himself. "Drunkenness, of one sort or another," he said, "is the ultimate romantic condition. As an authority, you should know that, Herr Professor, but you don't. You know nothing, really, except the perpetuation of your career, and whether you come from Missouri or Heidelberg is no matter—what you mainly want to establish is the eminence of Grosbeck the master scholar, the Authority. Power—you love it as long as it is on your side. Whether you like to admit it or not, your native element was Hitler's Germany . . . ."

George Willett stepped in front of McLoon and raised a glass. "Never mind it, Mac." He smiled blandly right and left. His tone was the one we use for drunks and madmen, kind and quiet and perfectly reasonable. "You aren't being fair to our host's wonderful Scotch." Willett of course was in his element as a referee. His face shone with good will and manliness. Everything about him expressed sincerity, the button-down oxford shirt and the tie with slanting stripes, the herringbone tweed jacket, the pink health of his cheeks, the clipped white-blond hair, the ready smile and fine teeth.

McLoon glanced down at him with a remote expression, like an old crocodile. "Up the varsity, eh?" he muttered in a voice beginning to blur. "Ole Cap'n Willett . . . ."

But then Grosbeck took over. He had stood quite still for a few seconds, and when he spoke the effect was almost like a shot going off. His voice rang out. "Whether you are drunk or not drunk, McLoon, I will not stand for this deliberate vilification." The words as recorded may sound composed and rational, but the voice shook with passion. His white face was spotted with red. "What you imply about me is slanderous. You have an evil tongue and a malicious mind. I am perfectly willing to share my views with my colleagues or anyone else, but your attack on me is too contemptible to reply to. You are in my judgment unworthy to fill the position that you presumably occupy."

I don't know how far this speech penetrated McLoon's consciousness. His dour and seamy face expressed nothing that it hadn't expressed before; the hooded triangular eyes seemed quite unconcerned with the present goings-on. But the rest of us were for a minute electrified—and I for one was frightened. Those literate words of Grosbeck's were uttered with an intensity that implied the farthest extremity of passion. Something in his tone sounded nakedly murderous, as though he were on the very edge of an insane onslaught, not only against McLoon but against all of us.

Perhaps I am being fanciful. I am not used to strong emotion and am unable to deal with it. As I said, I cry too easily, or lose my wits. It seemed amazing to me that Grosbeck could deliver a formal and rational address in tones and accents suitable for a Lear cursing his daughters. The two men, in fact, facing each other, represented human potentials that scared me—not only the personal intensities or passions of their natures, but the intellectual armament they commanded, the words they could utter as deadly as bullets. I think of all the others I have seen standing up under attack, giving and taking the deadliest blows like fighters in the ring, summoning up resources of fury and nerve that I could only wonder at.

"Self-esteem," McLoon said, and jerked his hand with the

glass in it so that an ice cube flew off to the parquet floor. "Shelf-esteem, that's all it is, old boy. Anyone suggests you aren't God's anointed scholar, you want to kill him dead. Me first, eh?" He waved the empty glass. "Ex-terminate 'em, eh?"

Even in his blurry state he was formidable. He didn't smile—I don't think he ever smiled.

"Truth!" he called out in a loud voice. "Who can stand it? Regard me, brothers 'n sisters. A man of truth. Be warned. Whom the gods destroy they—"

By then the shock had begun to pass. Voices spoke. Willett once again got in front of McLoon to turn him off. Mrs. Medrick said, "Do let's not squabble."

Grosbeck turned to go, still white and trembly. He spoke at the door. "I ask you to witness that this attack was unprovoked and malicious and monstrous. If you excuse it on the grounds of drunkenness or irresponsibility you will be condoning it. The malice is quite carefully calculated, I assure you."

"Oh, dear," Mrs. Medrick said in the vacuum that followed his departure, "this is really worse than the State House. I go to hearings, you know, and the things they *say* to each other—"

She did well. The old-fashioned Boston hostess may seem ludicrous, but she keeps things going. Even Willett said the wrong thing. "I'm so sorry, Mrs. Medrick. It was really quite outrageous . . ." We were all embarrassed enough without having it rubbed in. And as I said, I had even felt a shock of fear and perhaps awe at the sight of such furies.

But parties go on. We felt rather subdued for a while, as though we had been all publicly naughty, but drinks circulated, McLoon disappeared, and Medrick moved among us with his peculiar blend of charm and grandeur.

At the end Harriet took over for a little scene of her own. It is always a question how such parties should end, of course. The conservative and respectable ones leave at a suitable time between six and seven, and I'm sure the Medricks hoped we all would. But with some it is a point of honor to stay on, to eat and drink and talk indefinitely, perhaps to achieve an ultimate conviviality. Harriet used to be such a one. It's when they let their hair down, she said—and she wanted to be in on it. My impulse to leave early annoyed her. Lately she has been more agreeable about it, and I realize that she is no longer charmed by youthful indiscretion. "They think I'm an old witch," she said. It was along about seven-thirty, and she raised the last of her martinis. "Ladies and gents, I wish to propose a nomination." There were only a few of the drinking ones left and they looked at her with great good nature. "For the departmental Hall of Fame," she said in an oracular voice. "That man of courage, that walking heroic tragedy, that—" She stopped and re-gathered her wits. "What I mean is that ole son of a bitch, Angus McLoon. Whatever happened to him? I'm all for giving him a medal."

Mrs. Medrick was in the kitchen, luckily. The others there were ready to laugh at anything (Willett, incidentally, had gone earlier). "Down with the Fascists," Dunlin cried with cheerful irony.

I smiled too, but I tried to say it wasn't fair. I said it to young Arthur Merlin, our poet, who was standing next to me. But he hardly paid attention. He was joining the toast.

"Of course it wasn't fair," Harriet said later, when we got home. "But old McLoon is a character, isn't he? And as for Grosbeck, I simply can't stand him." She thought it over for a few moments. "You're always being 'fair.' It's such a bore."

❧ CHAPTER 7 ❧

WE HAVE ALSO A dinner-party circuit, which Harriet finds a bore—or at least pretends to. She can't stand these people or those people, as she says whenever the subject comes up, but actually her most intense pleasure is people. Any people—postmen, garbage collectors, parish visitors, old or young: she plays to any audience, trying for surprise or shock or admiration. She is pleased with children, at least when they come to the door, and speaks to them philosophically, as though they knew all about everything. With the grave and reverend she is apt to be ribald, and smokes cigarettes in a long holder and exhibits herself in red slacks. In any affair of art or esthetics she is very dogmatic and disrespectful, and attacks whatever is fashionable.

But in the course of a winter season we are invited here and there—not often, I must say, because we are an odd couple, and I'm sure my habit of uttering hopeful clichés is dampening, and I suspect Harriet's habit of needling me is embarrassing to some. But our more dutiful colleagues, like the Partridges and the Fulmars, invite us at suitable intervals, and of course we have to reciprocate, though we do so less faithfully. In her younger days she could plan and execute parties of all sorts, and was known for her exotic dinners, but the adventure of it seemed to dwindle and now she hates the effort and sneers at the stupid protocol of it all. Preserve us from Partridges and Fulmars, she says.

Yet now and then she gets herself cranked up to it, though after the last one she said she was through forever. We had the Fulmars as a matter of duty and the Buntings for somewhat the same reason, though they were a pleasant couple ("a *nice* couple," she said with characteristic scorn), and we had a man named Twachtman from the Art Department, and a young instructor of ours named Eliot Fitch who was said to be "doing work" in contemporary drama. We also had Evelyn Piper, who came very often to our house and was a steady friend and shadow of Harriet's.

Evelyn, I should explain, was for some reason necessary to Harriet's existence. They supplemented each other in a positive-negative relationship. Evelyn had been taught to be timid and nice, and she had no purpose in life; perhaps the slight deformity in her spine had confirmed her in virginity, or perhaps her long attendance on her widower father, who was as timid and nice as she was. He had retired before his time simply out of modesty; the young scholars, he told me with cheerful candor, were too much for him—they made him realize he was an impostor. He had no function, he dwindled away and "failed," as his friends put it. But he had a sweet humor and many spoke of him with affection—I think he had more devoted students than any of us. Evelyn was very like him, but had never got started and even though she had dutifully gone through college, as a professor's daughter was expected to, she remained safely at home—and since "home" was a five-room apartment on a third floor walk-up in Brookline she had little scope. Her one sustaining adventure was Harriet, that explosive, prejudiced, difficult creature—and the truth is that the adventure was not all on one side. Each gave the other happiness. There was no end to Evelyn's good nature and loyalty and eagerness in the small daily ventures of life. Our home was always pleasanter when she was in it. Harriet was better natured, everything was better taken care of, dinner parties usually went off smoothly. I think every household should have an Evelyn Piper in it.

Dr. Twachtman came late, and said he hadn't been able to find the house. Harriet at once pointed out that I was perfectly futile at giving directions. "He really hopes you'll lose yourself forever in the uncharted wilderness of Newton," she said so that all could hear.

"Well, it *does* seem to be pretty *wild country*," he said. "The streets all go round in *circles* and *loops*." He spoke as though he had said something with special wit and point, and I could see Harriet eyeing him with contempt, though he had no inkling of it. Yet she was stimulated by him. She seemed to glitter.

"I tell him," she said, nodding toward me, "to draw a little map and have it multigraphed, or whatever you call it, but no—he wants you to go round and round the loops."

In a way I realize that her humorous scorn of me was merely her way of being theatrical. Social folk are always trying to be funny, one way or another—just as Twachtman, for example, accented his words in the hope that he was being clever.

"Oh, I kept passing the same dreadful *house*," he said. "A sort of shingly tower on one end, actually *crenellated*. It was really an experience, I must say."

Harriet had said she was fed-up with English Department people: let's be daring, she said; let's ask that new art man—the one who did the book on Matisse—no wife to bother about—he can brighten up Evelyn's life a bit. One of our perennial jests was the mating of Evelyn, who was approaching her forties. Two men we had for her, Harriet noted—though Fitch was a bit young. But Dr. Twachtman . . . .

He was the kind you called doctor—I don't know quite why, except that he was tall and pale and wore rimless glasses. He looked doctoral. He wore a starchy shirt, and a dark gray tie with the kind of elegant knot I've never learned how to tie—though I've tried often enough (in secret, of course). I mean to ask some well-dressed acquaintance how he does it, but Twachtman was certainly not the one to ask. There's something about doctoral people that sets them apart—they are pale and intense and rather thin, and they wear neat and somewhat formal clothes and shoes with thin leather soles. They are serious, of course—for all the humorous accents in his talk, Twachtman was very touchy on professional matters. He was "doing work," it seemed, in the psychology of color. He performed laboratory experiments. He used a computer. He drew up charts and scales. He based everything on Matisse—a "great colorist," as he kept saying, and when Harriet advanced the theory that Matisse's work was mostly a spontaneous mess he settled down to a ten-minute lecture on its extraordinary craftsmanship and premeditated symbolism. "We have his successive *studies* of the same *composition*, you see, and we can analyze how his ideas *develop*—"

"Academic eyewash," Harriet said—not brutally, as it sounds, but with a humorous glitter, watching to see the result. "You all make your living out of this stuff. Modern art is mostly kids doing stunts on the back fence—see me, see what I can do, watch this—look, no hands—I'll bet your Matisse was just splashing round for the fun of it. How's that for color—beat that if you can!"

But of course Twachtman had heard all those arguments; he was briefed. "Yes, yes indeed, Mrs. Sanderling—"

"Oh, make it Harriet. For the fun of it. I'm all for fun— I'm all for splash too. I just don't think there's any point in writing dissertations about it."

It takes more than that to disconcert a doctor. "Ah, but man is what he is. The spontaneous mess, as you call it, may be more deeply *significant* than the rational and calculated. All values are not necessarily *intellectual* values, though we academic folk must try to express them in intellectual terms."

I thought it was a good speech, and though he still accented his key words he did it without the affectation of wit which he ordinarily had.

"That's it," Harriet came back. "It's your way of making a living. Those intellectual terms, as you call them, are sometimes pretty damned silly."

"But Professor—er—Sanderling," he said, waving at me. "Do you also feel that the academic effort is *silly?*"

Since my colleagues seldom asked for my views about anything I was caught quite unprepared. There was much to be said on both sides—I knew that, of course.

"Oh, I can tell you what Sandy thinks," Harriet said. "He thinks there's much to be said on both sides."

They all did call me Sandy, young and old—even my daughter Joan. It has a jaunty sound, and implies freckles and blond hair and a Scottish look which I certainly didn't have, but I confess that I've always enjoyed being called that,

and Twachtman's measured "Professor—er—Sanderling"
struck me as palpably phoney. I noticed that his silk socks
were pulled up very neatly round his thin ankles, and had
embroidered clocks. He must have worn garters. I was annoyed at him for his neatness. He was an indoor man, a figurine for a library or drawing room, an academic doctor.

It was a foolish attitude. He had every right to wear silk
socks and garters and to work in libraries, and it was perfectly
natural and suitable for him to call me Professor Sanderling.
The knot of his tie was certainly superior to anything I could
achieve. Yet he was the kind of man a sophomore would
consider phoney, and I couldn't help accepting that verdict.
But what I really felt as a hurt, like a shot of neuralgic pain,
was the confidential tone of Harriet's remark to him. I knew
she despised him, as of course she despised most people, as a
sort of policy if nothing else, and she was using him to bring
out her view of my failure.

"Sandy has a terrible time in restaurants," she said.
"Whether chicken or swordfish or good old hamburgers—it's
an awful decision. Don't ask him to decide about anything
major." She laughed with ironic calculation—a *ha ha ha*
sound.

I have to agree with her, in a way. I like to think I am not
indifferent, not a Laodicean, to use the bookish term, but
again and again I see that decisions are based not on "truth"
but on illusion. Twachtman's opinion of Matisse seemed to
me a great illusion—by which I mean that he believed in it
so devoutly that he built his life around it. He could as well
have "believed in" the beauty and truth of Indian totem
poles, and have spent his life computing their psychological
significance. What he defined as beauty, or esthetic value, as
he would call it, was his own rationalizing on the given stuff,

whatever it happened to be. Henry James used to call it the "donnée," and chose it with care, but now it doesn't seem to matter what the stuff is. Anyway, I can't help seeing both sides of most questions, or many sides, and a good arguer can persuade me to almost anything. Twachtman, I felt, was not a good arguer, and his views on Matisse did strike me as academic eyewash, as Harriet said; but a competent man could probably convince me that Matisse was the greatest painter of his time.

There wasn't much point in my trying to say anything, of course. Harriet had forestalled me. Some academic effort was pretty silly, I mumbled; some wasn't.

"Sandy prefers no effort at all," she said. She had a low-pitched vibrant voice with sardonic overtones, and she made the words sound amusing.

How one takes this sort of thing depends on the feeling of the moment—you can smile or shrug or flare up in anger. Since we had finished dinner and were mellow, it wasn't too bad. I said that my observation of mankind convinced me that the universal preference was to live without effort.

But Harriet seemed determined. If universal preference had prevailed, she said, we'd all still be apes. Some effort may be silly, like studying beauty with a computer, but almost any effort is better than none. She drew out the others. What did Fulmar think? What did Eliot Fitch think?

"Effort!" Mrs. Fulmar said. "You just don't know. He's at it night and day. The only time I see him is when we get invited out to dinner." She had a tinny loud voice, not suitable for academic company. Evelyn Piper tried to say that the results surely justified the effort, but no one paid much attention to her. She was a bright, cheerful and sensible woman, but people seldom listened to anything she said.

"Tell us, Rufus," Harriet said. "Why do you work so hard?" That was Fulmar's first name. Rufus. He was an old-timer with us—but the tendency is now toward first names at once. Young Fitch was new, but we naturally addressed him as Eliot. But with Twachtman there was still a barrier: the rimless glasses and store-window clothes gave us pause. I think his first name was Theodore, anyway. And he belonged to another department. But I must say the first-name habit, as practiced in America, is childish and even vulgar. I admired the way Grosbeck used our last names, simply and strongly, with no nonsense. After twenty years of association he still called me Sanderling.

So Harriet said Rufus, with a little rasp of accent to suggest that it was a rather preposterous name. "Why do you work so hard?"

He was not one to admit that anything he did was silly, but I supposed he had no idea why he worked. Except of course that he had a position to maintain.

"I believe in knowledge," he said with quiet intensity. It is always a surprise when a professional scholar gives a flat and serious answer to anything, but Fulmar was one of the most serious among us, and his intensity amounted almost to a nervous disorder. He twitched and blinked and held in some of his words until they seemed to break out by force.

"I bet when you were young you were told that knowledge is power," Harriet said. "You got the message in a Chinese fortune cooky."

He smiled on the left side of his mouth. "When I was young I read Boswell's Johnson, and I decided I'd like to be another Johnson. That was a more dr-drastic experience even than reading a message in a Chinese cooky."

"Are you still working at it—being another Dr. Johnson, I

mean?" You could say she was needling him, and I squirmed a little, though I recognized that her candor was really not malicious. She had no intent to inflict hurt on most people. She was merely impatient with pretense.

"I'm working at knowledge," he said.

I came out inevitably with what I realized was a rather fatuous remark. Eighteenth century scholars, I said, had given us much new knowledge lately—I alluded to the Walpole papers, the Boswell papers, the recent life of Mary Wortley Montagu. I reminded the company that Fulmar had done an edition of the letters of the Countess of Hartford . . . .

"No," Fulmar broke in suddenly. "I can't say it is very much use. It adds a few minor scraps, that's all. But we do what we can. We take pride in doing it well. We—" He stopped as though he realized there was no need to go on.

She shrugged with a little gesture of resignation as if to say that you can't needle an honest and dedicated man. Her smile took me in. "Pride," she said.

Our dinners, I must explain, were usually rather dull. No one ever drank too much, or carried on melodramatic intrigue. Harriet, as you see, did try to stir up trouble—mainly out of boredom and impatience with me. She called it getting a rise out of people.

She tackled Fitch on the subject of theatre, which she looked upon as her own field. What did *he* work for, she asked.

Fitch was the sort of man an English department doesn't quite know what to do with. He taught courses in drama, but he represented not the stuff of scholarship but the mystique of the theatre. He was said to be working for his doctorate (I hear Willett's confident voice using the phrase), but it was rumored among us that he had associated with Sir John Gielgud, had appeared on Broadway, and aimed to "do his thesis" on Berthold Brecht. The word "mystique" is appropriate to such people. They live and work apart from the rest of us with a priestlike sense of compulsive dedication. Nothing in the conventional world matters to them. They can be blandly arrogant. The "theatre" is the only thing that counts.

"I suppose I work for the coming of a new theatre," he said. "Specially in America."

It sounded good. I could see that Harriet wanted to accept him as a kindred spirit, though I realized that he was too pretty for her. He was tall, rather slender, with light curly hair—clearly a sensitive type. But he had a fine baritone voice. He had played Laertes, they said. But she took him up on this "new theatre" business.

It always sounds good, she said. The *new* art, the *new* novel, the *new* mouthwash.

Well, the new theatre, he felt, was the theatre of man's despair.

Was it new? And if so, why was it important? She had begun to gird herself for combat.

I must say there was an air of condescension about him, possibly coming more from the curly hair than anything else. He alluded to the "significant" modern dramatists, mentioned Brecht and others, deplored commercialism and the "Broadway syndrome," and then remarked that the only significant truth about modern man was his utter failure.

"Are you an utter failure?" Harriet asked.

That wasn't really the point, he said. Modern man . . . .

"Well, let's see," she went on, girding herself, as I said, "how about Rufus? I suppose he's just an eighteenth century type: let's say he failed to be Dr. Johnson, but after all that hardly counts. He's quite a man in his field, I'm told." When Harriet smiled a certain way she could be beautiful. "Or Dr. Twachtman—are you a failure, doctor—I mean an utter one? I bet you don't really think so." Her smile changed, became sardonic. "Of course, there's old Sandy here—you might study him. But I notice he could sit up and eat a pretty good dinner—"

By this time Fitch was flushed with irritation.

It wasn't a question of this or that individual, he said. But surely any student of modern man (he gave the phrase a raspy sort of emphasis) realized that he had lost his individuality and his function—and certainly he had lost his faith—

"Have you?" she asked again.

"It's quite irrelevant what I—"

"Damn it, it's not irrelevant. You're a man, aren't you? As far as I can see you've got plenty of function. I doubt if you need worry about your individuality—I really doubt if you do worry about it. Who the hell *is* this modern man you're so sorry for?"

Fitch stood up to the attack pretty well, but he was obviously astonished. Among millions, he tried to say, there was no belief in God or anything divine, no conviction that life was worth living or that what we used to call the "good" was worth struggling for. Man saw himself simply as a helpless organism—

In the first place, she said, the whole thing was mostly an abstract notion whomped up by a bunch of self-pitying intellectuals—and there was nothing "new" in it anyway. Anyone brought up on Thomas Hardy, the way her generation was, knew all about it. And secondly, what the hell good did it do to make a new theatre out of it? Why was it important to make plays about people who did nothing but feel sorry for themselves?

Since I felt rather sorry for Eliot Fitch at this point I tried to break in. The question, I said, was whether or not the play was a good play. But of course that was too obvious—I realized at once that it was a cliché.

Fitch was so flustered that he didn't hear anyway. He was trying to say that since Harriet was a lady living in Newton, Massachusetts, she obviously had no right to express opinion about the modern theatre. In fact, the whole popular and conventional attitude toward the theatre, as expressed by the commercial mass media, was destroying its function and life.

It was evident that he accused us all of being enemies of true art, but it was also evident that he saw us as incapable of change. The Newton syndrome, he implied, was hopeless.

Harriet didn't usually get mad at this sort of thing. She enjoyed it. If Fitch had handled it right she might have taken his side. As it was she laughed. "My God, I haven't been called a lady in thirty years. If you called Sandy a gentleman, there'd be some point to it—but me a lady! You live in a delusion, my boy, like those characters you hear about in western Canada who express their faith by hating the world and going naked. Some day you'll be marching round with signs: Down with the Mass Media, Down with Newton Ladies, Support the Theatre of Despair!"

Fitch was hurt, I could see. He was ready to strike out, but hardly knew where to begin.

Bunting, who was smoking a pipe, said we all lived in delusions, didn't we?

I had almost forgotten that the Buntings were there. She hardly said anything, and took refuge beside Evelyn Piper. But Arthur Bunting always looked as though he were about to speak wisely—a characteristic look of pipe-smokers. He was a thick man with a mustache and an air of solidity, but so reticent that we never knew how he felt about anything. I naturally wonder what goes on in other classrooms, and I picture Bunting's as a sort of Quaker Meeting with long intervals of silence. But he had published a difficult book on Wallace Stevens, the poet, (his doctor's thesis) and was regarded as a very sound man.

Everything, he said, is only what we imagine it is: like the stage. But he said it with the kind of irony that evades commitment. He didn't much care, one way or another.

But Eliot Fitch had had time to work up his anger. Along with suburban complacence you had academic complacence, which was worse. He regarded himself, it seemed, as of a calibre quite different from the rest of us. His theatre was something "real." It was out there where men lived and struggled and of course failed. He leaped to his feet and paced the floor. He mentioned the miseries and brutalities of mankind, the actualities of man's plight—as contrasted with this bland and insulated ease. He waved his arm. He spoke out with Shakespearean force. The new theatre is one place where the truth must be spoken—it is almost the only place where it can be spoken. The rest of us, whether we know it or not, are in the grip of the profit system. Our notion of good drama was probably something nice by James M. Barrie . . . .

I thought Harriet would laugh again and perhaps applaud, but it seems that Fitch was more than she could put up with. She could be amused at being called a lady, but to impugn her taste in drama was too much for her. "For heaven's sake, young fellow, will you pipe down! You talk like a Greenwich Village sophomore—and you are supposed to be old enough to teach in a grown-up university. You behave the way all these half-witted demonstrators do—you stand up and denounce everybody." She spoke quite mildly, but the accent was sardonic.

I suppose she was right. Young Fitch had no business letting go like that, specially at a dinner party—though she had needled him rather cruelly. And he did tend to "denounce everybody," as she said. I knew he had done some demonstrating for various causes. It struck me as naïve of him to insist on man's futility and helplessness on the one hand, as though that were the most vital truth, and to advocate political or social action on the other. But I could see that it all related somehow to his vision of a new drama that would sweep away the evasions and hypocrisies of the past.

At any rate, our little party was pretty well upset. Fitch, after his denunciations and Harriet's scolding, hardly knew what to do. He couldn't simply sit down and resume conversation. He couldn't renounce the truths he had uttered. Yet he feared he had made a fool of himself.

"I'd better go," he said. "I'm sorry I upset you. I guess I shouldn't have—I mean I—well, thanks for asking me—that is, dinner and all." He looked about with a flushed dignity, trying to make the best of himself.

I followed him to the hall, and spoke the necessary platitudes. I may have said that I admired his dedication to the new drama—though I don't think I went so far as to say the "drama of despair." My own view, for what it is worth, is that when you make a cult of despair or futility or any such thing you are being foolish, but I didn't say so. Actually young Fitch took a sort of pleasure in promoting the idea—it had become a "philosophy" for him and probably gave him status among his associates. Illusion, as Bunting said—it is what we live by, or in.

I returned to the living room intending to take him up on it. I rehearsed a question or two. Weren't there good illusions and bad illusions, and wasn't it necessary—? but I realized suddenly that "necessary" was the wrong word. It implied moral necessity, which no modern thinker would accept. Wasn't it *desirable* to try to evaluate illusions? I tried to think of what I knew about Wallace Stevens, the subject of Bunting's book, and had only a confused notion of some fanciful theories and images. Conscience pricked me. I must *get at* Stevens . . . .

"I do like that young idiot," Harriet was saying. "If he weren't such a damn fool I'd agree with him—I mean I'm in favor of a new drama or a new anything. And this suburban frog-pond we live in—my God, look at Sandy there, after a lifetime in Newton: he hasn't had a new idea in half a century."

"Oh come, Harriet—how you talk!" Evelyn laughed brightly.

The others were embarrassed, and rose to go with the usual pleasantries. The Fulmars knew what to expect from Harriet, and Bunting put on the careful look of a man playing poker, but Twachtman was quite nervous about his goodbyes. I'm sure he meant to steer clear of Harriet in the future.

꧁ CHAPTER 8 ꧂

I CAN REALIZE what dull good people my parents were, but I look at that life with affection and respect. From a distance of fifty years it seems fixed, like a scene from Currier and Ives. What "new ideas" there were had to do with putting in a telephone or electric wiring or steam heat, and eventually of buying an automobile, but the beliefs and customs were changeless, or so it seems as I summon up my remembrance. Religion meant the Sunday service at the Congregational Church, and nightly prayers rattled off by habit—also the family Bible with names and dates recorded on the fly leaves. Also good clothes on Sunday, and no card playing. Good behavior meant strict adherence to the manners and codes, and no one had the slightest doubt as to what was right and wrong. If wrong were done, it was done in secret and with shame. The propaganda for the right was incessant: parents and teachers and speakers all advocated the morally good and denounced the bad. Life was seen as a clearly marked road toward respectability and family rectitude.

These notes are not derived from common knowledge, as

it were, but are evoked by my father's vest and watch chain, and his starched collar, and his black derby hat which he exchanged for a straw boater on May fifteenth. What secret yearnings he had are beyond my knowing. The man I remember was a pattern of control and caution. No smoking or drinking or disappearing at night, no misery—and no gladness. He did his duty and lived his life. Harriet likes to say I am just like him, but she is wrong.

He came down from Vermont to be a clerk in a Boston bank, leaving the farm and country ways. He dressed for the city, was virtuous and reliable, got a better job with a real estate firm, and in time became manager of their Newton branch. That's his career.

With a wife of equal virtue, a daughter of the church he attended. I cannot overstate the virtue. When I went to college and read *Tom Jones* my mother wept. Yet she was not self-righteous, not grim and accusing: she lived in that state of paradoxical innocence that saw evil in almost everything. She poignantly explained to me, when I was ten or less, that every time I cried "gee," or "gee whizz" I was uttering blasphemy, and she had the same attitude toward any natural bodily function that related to sex. These opinions are well known, of course, but are often scornfully related to bigotry. My mother was a very sweet person. As a boy I loved her. As a young man in college I was embarrassed and constrained by her, and found it hard to talk freely with her, but I loved her. By the time she was an elderly widow she didn't try to talk at all, except for the gossip and trivialities of the moment, and lived for a year with us after we were married—always sweet, undemanding, somehow untouched by anything.

When I described my old colleague Partridge and his ways I was thinking somewhat of the Vermont Sanderlings too.

Partridge is a very able man, and full of the complacence that comes with success and long-sustained virtue, but he represents a class that used to be prominent in our region. In an older country it would be called the yeomanry. The basis of it was the substantial farmer, the owner of fields and woods and clapboard buildings, the deacon, the selectman, sometimes the reluctant candidate for county or state office. In my boyhood in and about Newton it seemed to me that a great many people we knew, the shopkeepers or the doctors or lawyers, were closely linked with those substantial country folk. Everyone had grandparents and cousins up in the hills somewhere, and kept open the old lines of interest and love. We always expected a barrel of winter apples in October, and gallons of maple syrup in April, and incidental pickles and relishes, along with hand-knitted wool mufflers and socks. My father was an unsentimental man, but he always felt that he "lived" up there in Allensville, and this suburban life hardly seemed real to him. He subscribed to a Rutland paper and kept up with the deaths and births and other changes. He took us home, as he called it, for summer visits, and spent endless hours talking with his brothers and the old folks, going over and over all the local gossip and recalling the life of half a century. The visits, in fact, were taken for granted as a yearly routine: "We'll be going for the Fourth, as usual," he always said—and of course it was an anxious and vivid journey by trolley to the North Station and train up through Keene and Bellows Falls and on into the far mountains.

A long, long way, it seemed to me. The engine puffed and chugged and blew long country whistles, smoke and cinders filled the hot cars, we stopped for silent waits at lonely stations where empty milk cans were unloaded. The sun was always hot, the air always still, the hill country lay all about like a vast mystery. I remember my landmarks, the rush and falls of the Connecticut where we crossed it, the running brook where we climbed and climbed with slower puffs and heavier chugs—and then the "height of land," as my father called it, where the train eased along and stopped at a station so remote that no one seemed to be there at all—though if I got close to the window and looked ahead I could see a farm wagon backed in against a loading platform. And beyond that a mountain with two humps in the summer sky, and dark forests of spruce.

Then the rattley rush downgrade to Allensville, and Uncle Jeff waiting with the team and wagon—a three-seat carry-all and a pair of young Morgans. Automobiles were occasionally seen in the valley towns then, but were not able to cope with mountain roads—and we knew that a capable farmer prized a good matched team above all things. Uncle Jeff was really running the farm during these years, and the Morgans were what he chiefly lived for. Not that the Sanderlings were ostentatious, or even prosperous, but I think at that time the farm and the life of the farm seemed permanent. It had been there for a century and would go on for ever, and good cattle and horses were what a farm was built on. Actually Uncle Jeff was an ingrown and reticent bachelor, with nothing to do in the world except to work and devote himself to good cattle. He and my father looked quite a lot alike, and had a silent affinity for each other, but he was very shy with females and would hardly look at my mother or even my two sisters who were still children. The family always joked about his oddities and told little stories—mostly on the subject of his fear of women. I might add now that after the old folks died and he found himself alone on the farm he gradually grew queer and let everything go to pieces. That's one of the motives of the novel I wrote.

But he was patient with little boys and let me sit with him on the driver's seat and even pretend to hold the reins—and I can still feel how the power and energy of the Morgan horses seemed to flow into my small hands. There was a fairly level run up a valley for a couple of miles, and the team could speed along with a fast even trot—and Uncle Jeff took care to show off its paces: but then came the long climbing and the rough going and the slow grinding of the wheels up gravelly steeps. The powerful haunches worked, the flanks grew wet, heads bobbed, and nostrils flared and snorted.

The talk was all of local events—the death of old man Tucker, the planting of corn in Stoddard's lower meadow, the new sawmill up on the Flats, Ed Robertson's herd of registered Holsteins. Father leaned forward to hear what Uncle Jeff said above the creak and clatter of the wagon, but the speech was so cryptic and understated that I missed a good deal of the substance. Uncle Jeff never said more than he had to. He implied that things were going pretty badly: too little rain, wholesale milk prices too low, late spring set them back nearly a month . . . .

But for a boy from the suburbs the farm life was a day-long drama, from the dawn milking on through the rituals of tending cattle, harnessing work horses for cultivating—and what I remember best, haying. My cousins came, my Uncle Charlie came up from Allensville, there was a strong current of family spirit and we were all aware of the farm as a living entity that we were part of. They weren't jovial folk, those Sanderlings, but they depended on one another and had an unexpressed vision of a life that sustained itself by means of well-mowed fields and well-stored barns. I could be one of the three or four youngsters who trod the load on the haywagon—or later in the hot loft of the huge barn. My cousins were at times contemptuous of me as an outsider and an innocent—they tried to shock me with the primitive or even savage facts of farm life—but in the rituals of haying we seemed to be in harmony.

As for my two sisters, they were enough older to live in a different world. Long skirts, black stockings—no matter how hot it was—leather shoes with buttons (at least I seem to remember things like that): they weren't encouraged to romp on hay-wagons—and were actually subject to some cruelty from their male cousins. I should add that Abby, the older, died many years ago during her hospital training as a nurse. Julia married a young real estate operator who took her off to Florida to make a fortune, went broke in the thirties, recovered in the forties but died before he could achieve the wealth he dreamed of. Julia is still in Florida. I see her once in two years or so. She lives in a five-room "tract house," as she calls it, one of a hundred or so, and is quite snug and contented. Her son is a master sergeant in the regular army.

These details about the farm and the family have no special point in themselves, but they may suggest a kind of characteristic genesis. There was no excuse for my becoming a college professor. My people were not scholarly. They read very little. They were ordinary back-country farmers. And even in our suburban life we had very little to do with book learning. I had the usual public school education, but in those days getting into college was easy and I was able to go to Harvard as a day student. In one way I represent the dwindling away of a strong tradition. I assume that those Vermont forefathers were better men than I am—and I'm sure my grandfather, whom I knew, was a man of great moral and physical strength. And his father had been elected to the state legislature—and *his* father was still remembered in family annals as Deacon Sanderling. They are the ones we kept in mind. At least two were named Robert, and I take a little comfort in being linked to them, but I am certainly not one of them. When my father settled in Newton to deal in real estate he left his heritage behind him.

It seems to be assumed in our time, at least by critics and scholars, that all men fail. We have lost not only heritage but function and faith. It is almost as though we gloat on failure, and the tragedy of being a lost and desperate human consciousness were the last great experience worth commemorating.

My father, I think, considered himself a success. I suppose any trained observer could have pointed out his failings, his loss of "function," his retreat from commitment: even his lifelong dogmatic conservatism is evidence of his guilt. But as far as I could ever see he went through the motions of life with no regret and no grief—and even his dying was sustained by the old faith he never questioned. He worked dutifully, made a living, bought a house, paid off the mortgage, drove a Hudson Super-Six. He married respectably, was faithful, fathered three normal children, sent his son to college. He took pleasure in small comforts, installed good plumbing, a gas stove, and even, before he died, an oil furnace. He went "in town" to Boston every Saturday on a solitary outing, as though it were his duty, and spent the afternoon browsing in hardware stores and bargain basements. I believe he operated his real estate business as honorably as it is possible to, considering of course that the aim is to make a profit on all transactions. He was never a slick operator, a back-slapper or hearty handshaker, and he genuinely disliked the hypocrisies that were part of his business. But he was always a practical

man. He spoke well of a good trade or a nice profit. He felt
that any man deserved what he could legally get, and in his
view of society every man was on his own, responsible only to
law and his conscience. If he failed it was his own fault. Any
notion of social planning for the general welfare seemed as
foolish to him as trying to control the storms of winter or the
yearly cycle of the seasons. Men took their chances with what
they were given, and making the best or the worst of it was
up to them. There were poor and miserable folk in his Vermont country, of course, but it is fair to say that their misery
was partly their own choice. They lived in tar-paper shacks
because it was easy and even free: they could be as dirty and
irresponsible as they pleased, and no one interfered with
them. If they really wanted to, they could work their way
into respectability—but they chose to be what they were.

So—let them alone, he said. Let them be. Let social nature take its course.

Not that he thought much about it, or about anything. He
read the *Herald* every day. He kept up with baseball news
and real estate news. He devoted himself to his house and
grounds—and in that kind of work was a perfectionist: a
blister of paint was at once attended to, or a frayed sash cord
or squeaky floorboard; and he kept the quarter acre of ground
as precise as a checkerboard, with edges and plots and beds
all ruled and pure. All his country heritage was devoted to
tending a weedless lawn and the "plantings" suitable to the
house of a suburban real estate operator. In the back corner
of the lot, out of public sight, he nurtured a peach tree and a
patch of rhubarb, and set out a dozen tomato plants every
spring. At the end of his life he regretted that he hadn't established an asparagus bed. "That's the one thing," he
said—the one thing he hadn't got round to doing. He was

not a man for overwhelming regrets or guilt. How would my young critics judge him? A failure? "Weak?"

They wouldn't bother, I suppose. He signifies nothing to them. An old-fashioned suburban man, without much visible character. Quiet, predictable, set in his ways. A Mason. For a time church treasurer. Not much else. A dry man. Always neat and respectable, with vest, white collar, black shoes—even at his gardening he looked more city than country, though he wore his "old clothes" for that—the dark gray or blue serge he had once worn to the office. He never stepped out without a hat—when he mowed the lawn he wore a Panama, and in hottest weather an alpaca jacket.

But he did keep in touch with baseball, which in those days was the main sport of farm boys in Vermont and elsewhere. It was hard to imagine him or Uncle Jeff actually playing the game, but they had once been on an Allensville town team and had even gone to Rutland for a game on the fairgrounds—an event alluded to in many conversations. The major league teams of Boston were closely followed in every country village in New England—and I remember visits from my uncles and cousins who came to see the Braves play: for some reason they preferred the Braves to the Red Sox in those days. I think the National League used to seem more conservative and more suitable for Republican support.

So now and then he took me. But it was never a carefree or jovial affair. No shouting, no orgy of hot dogs and soft drinks, not even much conversation. We sat in silent attention and he made little notes on a score card. In later years when I occasionally took Joan I remembered how it had been with my father, and I made an effort to be different—we had ice cream and Cokes and we called out and cheered at critical plays, but I had a strong sense of being my father all over again, I felt his caution and reticence in me.

But in fact I had poor preparation for an academic life. No "ideas" existed in our house, no speculation as to how life might be designed. My mother lived from meal to meal in a state of innocence, and cherished all our old habits and properties with childlike sentiment. The house was a conglomeration of old shabby relics and new department-store pieces suitable to a successful real estate man of the early nineteen-twenties, and it wasn't until after I married and lived with Harriet that I realized what a stifling place it was. The walls and wood-work tended to be brown, the upholstery was mostly dark brown (a practical color), the furniture was a hit or miss collection of golden oak and wicker and what used to be called mission, and ornate lamps with pink shades and tassels, and gilt mantel clocks and souvenirs and empty vases and all the stuff that drifts into a house and never gets thrown away. I remember a sandal-wood fan, partly broken, and a green iron wolf with jaws designed for cracking nuts, and a bronzed model of the Eiffel Tower. The furnace and the plumbing worked well; the air was hot all winter, we had unlimited hot water; we had electric refrigeration before most people did, and a washing machine with a spinner. But few books.

It is one of the reasons I so often feel like an academic imposter—this early lack of book culture. Grosbeck, for example, seems to have been brought up to be a scholar: his father was the editor of an encyclopedia, his grandfather was a philosopher exiled from Germany. That's how great scholarship is carried on. But I did well in school—not ever brilliantly, but simply "well." Being a good student was a line of least resistance for me, and gave me pride and pleasure. I did my lessons, answered questions, attended all classes and meetings. I wrote essays and papers, became a minor editor on the school paper, and even in the end won a prize for English composition. I suppose I was the kind of student teachers like—a steady and faithful performer. But I was never conspicuous enough among my fellows even to be sneered at or accused of being a teacher's pet or a sissy or an oddity—I had a sort of cloak of invisibility, which perhaps I still have.

It is hard to know what the truth about these things is. I don't see the young Sandy of forty some years ago as lacking in good boyishness, or as taking refuge in the flattery of teachers. I played the games, I skated, coasted, had friends—I was not much of a fighter, but I could wrestle. I tried hard to be a distance runner. But perhaps I retreated too much. We had a fine public library, and I spent hours in it, doing lessons, reading, browsing. I read far too many novels, or perhaps too few good ones, but much of my adolescence was spent in the dream world of sentimental fiction. Who remembers Anthony Hope, or Robert W. Chambers, or George Barr McCutcheon?

Anyway, my father took it for granted that I would go to college, even to Harvard. He had made a good living for himself, he had improved his cultural status, and the next step was obviously to send his son to college. As I have said, he was a very practical man, and very conservative (or backward) in his social opinions, but he was also a simple honest man who hoped for the best for his children. He was very willing to pay my tuition and even a little extra.

So I went by day—a rather long trip by various trolley lines. I read so much in the jiggly car seats that presently I had to wear spectacles.

CHAPTER 9

I DON'T REALLY know very much about the Harvard world, except that in those days it paid no attention to an outsider like me. I had little more connection with it than, say, the man who swept down the library steps. I came and went there for a good part of eight years, and in the later years I "assisted" various professors—which I suppose gave me some sort of inner knowledge—but it embarrassed me to be described as a Harvard man. There were several pretty characteristic types—then and doubtless now too—and of course I could observe them in their outward affairs. The most conspicuous "type" was the old collegiate upper class, which is well known in all major colleges—more so then than now, perhaps. Some combination of manner, family, money, and prowess was needed. In its earliest days, two and three centuries ago, Harvard ranked its students in order of their social importance—by what divination the rankings were decided on I don't know, but the old habit persisted, and may still persist.

And to be candid, though I used to feel the indifference

and even disdain of those chosen ones, I liked their grace and style, the easy fit of their clothes, and the irony of their voices. I suppose culture and all it implies in art and books and manners would amount to little without an élite—at least that is a reasonable way of looking at history. I remember Winston Sanderson who sat next to me in a semester Shakespeare: no words were exchanged between us for a month, but then I began to build up a little picture of his life. Because of his nightly engagements he never slept enough, and dozed through class—it was his need for my notes that opened the communication between us. He felt miserable and unhappy from lack of sleep and too much evening liquor, and he used to groan and mutter about the ordeal of being alive. But he went to the Saturday night Symphony (one of the basic signs of cultural status), he was invited to teas to meet painters and poets, and he could run the hundred yards in under ten seconds. What interested me most was that he had the inside dope about everything. I took some pride in my faithful work as a student, but my innocence of the ways of the Harvard world was absurd. He could tell exactly what was coming on the exams. He knew "what they looked for" and how they graded. He knew what to study and what not to. He knew how to get an A on a term paper—he seemed to know all about "primary source material" and bibliographical subtleties. His uncle in Hamilton, he told me, was a collector, had a house full of first editions—stuff they didn't even have in Widener. I never found out what Sanderson got in the course, but it may well have been an A. He taught me a good deal about how to get along. I haven't seen him in all these years, but he was for a while our ambassador to various countries and was much admired for his work in Yugoslavia. When I read about him I feel in touch with great affairs.

But the ones I remember most vividly were the professional intellectuals—or perhaps I should call them the young prodigies. A small minority, but they appeared as undergraduates, were recognized as phenomena by their teachers and accepted as fellow scholars. They achieved brilliant success with what seemed like disdainful ease. They knew everything. Nor were they human freaks, in any bad sense. Perhaps a few were unbalanced—I haven't really enough evidence to report on them: the world expects prodigies to lack virility or common sense or ordinary affection. But in the academic arena they did wonders. I have always felt that my own background was inadequate for a university career such as mine, but for the greatly gifted it doesn't seem to matter.

In a class in Chaucer I sometimes found myself sitting next to a country boy named Trundy. I wondered at first how he had got in among the real students: he always smelled like an old farmhouse, his shirt was dirty and rumpled, and he spoke with the accents of northern Maine. He took no notes and sat there in a state of stolid indifference, and while I tended to dislike his smell and dirty shirt I worked up a good deal of sympathy for the plight of an innocent country boy quite out of his element, until one day Jackson, our celebrated professor, interrupted himself in a discussion of Petrarch to invite Mr. Trundy's comments on the sources of the Griselda story. The class as a whole seemed to know all about Trundy, but it was only then that I realized that he was "assisting" Professor Jackson. He came to the lectures simply to keep in touch with the progress of the class, but I was given to understand by others that he really knew more about the stuff than old Jackson. After that I watched him with a kind of awe, but some sort of jealousy or snobbishness made me dislike him: I began to think he was truculent, and had no feeling for the literature he had mastered. But I acknowledged that he knew everything.

That was the class where I heard about Gaw. And the name, when I think of it, reminds me of my innocence. The truculence I suspected in Trundy was really rather characteristic of the Harvard of that period—though come to think of it experts always tend to be impatient with fools and innocents. I was probably both. Jackson had cited Gaw a few times, and I remember noting the name with a question mark beside it: but then Gaw came in more and more, and I tried to find out who it was. No luck. No index listed Gaw. Yet it seemed to be assumed by our lecturer that we knew all about Gaw. Everyone accepted the name, no one questioned it.

I finally asked Trundy. "Who's this Gaw he keeps talking about?"

He shrugged with contempt. "Gaw," he said in a tone to imply that any fool knew that.

"Yes, but who is he?"

"John Gaw."

I suppose that was something. He condescended slightly. But his tone put an end to dialogue. We spoke no more. I remember his voice, though, after forty years: the back-country twang of it, as though it were tuned for calling cattle. John Gaw!

Of course I found out in time that they were talking about one John Gower, a learned poet of Chaucer's era, who wrote long unreadable poems with Latin titles—in fact I think I surprised my inquisitors on my doctor's orals by rattling off those Latin titles and discussing the substance as though I too were one of the prodigies. I've never forgotten John Gaw,

but why they called him that I never knew. It may be simply
that Yankees dislike the sound of r. It was said that one man
from Indiana failed his orals because he insisted on pronouncing the name as it is spelled.

But with all that brilliance and competence, there was a
good deal of misery. I did well enough because I simply
plugged along steadily. I suppose I didn't expect triumphs,
and was pleased to survive. I don't agree with my father's old-
time social views, but in a way I represent them. His is the
country attitude, even the frontier attitude, where a man has
to succeed by his own efforts, and I went to the university
with that point of view firmly in mind. I can see that ideally
it is an admirable theory of life, but it doesn't work out in
cities and ghettoes, or perhaps in the multiversities, as they
are now called. I did my duty, entered graduate school, became an "assistant," wrote a thesis, passed orals—all in order.
I did worry, I sat up all night finishing papers, I got B grades
instead of A—but my troubles were nothing to my friend
Koppel's.

Some of the outsiders tended to gravitate together, and
since I continued to commute daily I was an outsider. I had
no place to "go," no pleasant headquarters with what are
called facilities. I lived mostly in the library. When I
achieved some scholarly status I was given a desk and chair
among the stacks, a stall, as it was designated—and perhaps
it is reasonable to say that I learned about myself more in
those hours and years in the lonely labyrinth of books than at
any other time in my life. In a way it was like a prison, with
its endless ranks of steel stacks, and steel floors and stairways,
and day-long silence—except for the shuffling of footsteps on
the corridors, but the infinity of books gave it a fourth or
fifth dimension of mystery. I never achieved a systematic

scholarship, but I got to be a competent book-scout: if it were a question of the ground rules of a medieval tournament, or tracking down Chaucer's relatives by marriage, or finding out when sash weights were first used in windows (a Shandian problem), I could achieve results quickly. It may be that I have a more whimsical nature than I quite realize.

Koppel was a first-year graduate student with a stall next to mine, and for a long time we hardly even nodded to each other. He seemed furtive to me, and too dark, like a night creature. Clothes were black, hair was black, and he stooped over his books as though he naturally avoided the light. Very thin and unhealthy grayish looking, with dry hands and stringy little wrists that stuck out of his sleeves. When he wasn't there I took note of the books he used: drama, mostly—minor Elizabethans and Jacobeans, Dekker and Middleton and Shirley.

Eventually I broke the silence. Was he doing a paper for Ralston?

Furtive still. He wouldn't look at me. But he admitted the paper. He seemed to breathe hard when he talked.

Later I turned up a learned article on Shirley and the Comedy of Manners and brought it to him. And some days after that he made a little effort to thank me. He came by as I was working—he had a gangly half-sidewise shuffle, and sort of nodded as he passed, though his motions were so jerky, it was hard to tell whether he intended a nod; but then he turned back and thanked me in a little prepared speech which he recited with a look of suffering. It wasn't at all what he wanted, the article, but of course it had some interest for its own sake. "Thank you anyway, though."

That seemed to end our association for a while. But a few weeks later I found a scholarly journal on my desk with a note in it: "Here's a Smollett thing you've probably seen."

These amenities took about six months. Eventually we went out to lunch at a cafeteria.

He existed, I discovered very soon, in utter misery. He suffered, not from hunger or cold, but from the conviction that it was his duty and destiny to suffer. Harvard was naturally an establishment of selected snobs, and they despised anyone who couldn't say Gaw, or who pronounced the middle g in "singing." Anyone from the Bronx, as he was, with what was called a Jacob Riis Fellowship, was merely a nuisance to them.

I could share his feelings. Even an outsider from the respectable suburb of Newton felt similar miseries. It had never occurred to me to question the system, even if misery resulted: it was simply the world, where men fall into ranks and hierarchies. Sanderson had an uncle who collected first editions and other treasures. I didn't. Trundy had a prodigious intellect, which set him far above the rest of us. I suppose I suffered from various inequalities and inferiorities, but I tended to accept my lot as though it had been arranged by divine order.

Perhaps Koppel did too. He took satisfaction in being a fatal victim. But now, forty years later, the Koppels are in the forefront of protest—and some of the Sanderlings too. It is one of the greatest changes in human history—this refusal to accept the old order, whether divine or natural or simply habitual. What they protest against is partly man himself.

Koppel felt that his future depended on the grades he got in his courses, and so far he had had one C and three B's. That meant the edge of failure and the thought of it possessed him like a nightmare. But what counted was the year's grades, not the half year's, and he still had a chance. His greatest hope now, in the spring term, was that he would be "thrown out with a master's degree"—which is what happened to the ones not quite over the edge. For the graduate school world a "terminal master's degree," to use the common jargon, was the next thing to failure. The doctorate was the only victory worth fighting for. But Koppel had all but given up that hope. He plugged along in misery.

But I found that he had even less inside dope than I had ever had. He lived a wholly solitary life, treading the drab streets between the Harvard Yard and his third-floor tenement room near Central Square. He wouldn't of course speak to any knowledgeable insider who might sit next to him in class. He attended none of the meagre social events that were arranged for lonely graduate students. He took pride in having nothing to do with anybody. But he worked with what seemed to me agonizing persistence, all day and most of the night—I at least had other "interests"—I knew people, had friends and neighbors, I fell in love: but Koppel abandoned human affairs—he hardly ate, as I found out when I proposed lunch or supper. The darkness seemed to thicken round him as the year advanced. His stomach was bad, he said; he had post nasal drip and a boil on his neck.

Perhaps in the end I helped him get through, but it nearly killed him. In June he had wasted, he turned all damp and waxy, he drooped. I met him after his last exam—it was in Old French. I thought I could walk back to his room with him and perhaps sustain him somehow. He was so done in he couldn't seem to speak, and shuffled along with no sense of direction. I steered him into a lunch counter and ordered coffee, and we sat in a hopeless sort of silence. I suppose I simply felt sorry for him. He never allowed me to like him in the ordinary companionable ways of young men; he resisted sympathy and friendly aid. But I had taken him on, and perhaps was flattering myself that I was doing good.

"I'm expecting you back in the fall," I said.

He didn't speak or drink his coffee for some time. Then he said something about selling shoes. His father and his uncle, it seemed, had a shoe store in the Bronx. They quarreled a good deal, specially about him. It was his Uncle Joshua who had urged him through college and paid the bills. His father said he'd be more sensible to stick to the store—and the idea of going to graduate school at Harvard seemed crazy to him. And it *was* crazy, of course. He knew it all along. He should have had more sense.

"You don't know," I said. "You may pass—you may have done very well." I heard my own voice being hopeful.

"Pass is no good." He shrugged. "The fact is they don't want any Julius Koppel here."

I said that true scholars were not influenced by that kind of prejudice.

He perked up a bit, after sipping coffee. It struck me that his mind operated in one department and his instincts in another. True scholars were great men, he said. They were his gods. There were some at Harvard, and he asked for nothing more than the chance to learn from them: Ralston was such a one—a great man, intellectually a god; it was a privilege to be able to sit in his classroom. And learning itself, scholarship as I had said, had no class lines or race lines. But Harvard as a whole, the corporation as it was called, the system or establishment, that was intended for the acceptable cultured few, not for Julius Koppel. Privilege—name—family . . . he went on with intensity. He felt it the instant he came to register—not only the condescension but the unconcealed hope that he would fail. There was a silent but obvious conspiracy to get him out of there—the course assistants, the underlings, the other graduate students, all shared in it.

I had to admit that there was some justice in his opinions, but I found myself still trying to soothe him. They treated me the same way, I said. They treated everyone that way. It was a trial period, an initiation.

But he would have none of my soft soap. Look at the incompetents they pushed ahead: look at that prize ass, Waldo Holworthy, the pet of the department—what did he ever do but cultivate his Oxford accent? Even the great Professor Jackson was less a scholar than a gentleman of family and property, with a house on Brattle Street and an estate up in New Hampshire somewhere.

It made him feel better to be complaining again, but the return to his dismal room bowed him down with woe. They'd all be disappointed, of course—his Uncle Josh who had spent so much on him, his mother, his grandparents, his aunts and his cousins, even his father who had told him all along it was no good. He turned away from me, rejected my clichés of comfort, ushered me out. "Leave me alone, Sandy. It isn't worth bothering about. It's what I expected. I'll send you news from the shoe store. That's how I got into Elizabethan Drama, you know—I thought *The Shoemaker's Holiday* was for me. You can see what a fool I was."

But of course he came back. He suffered through three years of it, passed his orals, got his degree, is now a professor at Illinois State, with a modest list of publications to his credit. A grim sort of man, I think—and probably very hard on his students. No sense in encouraging incompetents, he says.

His ordeal at Harvard may have been worse than mine, but together we probably stand as representatives of all the unprotected innocents who used to come there. Today there are not so many innocents. The training of scholars is recognized as a tough professional discipline, with few pleasurable amenities. The competition may be fiercer but the conditions are more clearly seen. No one expects to thrive because of his name or his good taste or his accent.

I met Koppel not long ago when he came east for some meetings. He is known in the profession chiefly for his studies of the psychology of sex in early Jacobean drama, and his ferretlike intensity about that and all other matters somewhat embarrassed me. He regarded me, I suspected, as no better than a minor dilettante; I realized that he had drawn up a sort of agenda for himself which involved consultation with the more distinguished of our assembled colleagues. But I did sit with him at a meeting and we chatted a little about old times. They were great men, he said; those were the classic days of scholarship, and we were fortunate to have been part of them. He spoke the names with reverence: Kittredge, Lowes, Grandgent. He had done his thesis under Ralston, of course. And did I realize that Jackson was still living on his New Hampshire estate—he must be in his nineties. A wonderful man, a scholar and a gentleman. Of course Trundy was an able scholar in the field, but he never had the sort of *quality* the older men had—and frankly most of these new younger men were simply specialists . . . .

He murmured these opinions in lowest tones, glancing a bit nervously right and left. He no longer had the furtive look of a night creature, but he was very gray and wizened and anxious, and his heavy spectacles were continually turning one way or another. We have a great responsibility, he said, to keep up the old standards.

He was a very serious man. I intended to speak facetiously about John Gaw, but the opportunity never came.

≈§   CHAPTER 10   §≈

OUR DEPARTMENT does have doctorate candidates, of course, and it is a serious matter indeed. We are not Harvard, but we do our best. Willett, our leader, is as earnest about it as a varsity football coach, and talks about "bringing his man along," and "watching him develop confidence." He is always going over the basic requirements for the degree, and summoning committees to consider this or that alteration. He is a conservative man, and admires the old traditions, but he keeps a close watch on other universities. "There's a good deal of new thinking about this," he will say. "Out at Chicago, I hear—" And then Jaeger will say "Chicago!" in a tone of contempt and will utter a quick grim laugh that dismisses Chicago forever from the consideration of intelligent men. Or it might be Cornell or California—or anywhere.

But the phrase "new thinking" always makes us uneasy. We all read the articles that come out weekly and monthly in the best magazines: "The Shame of the Graduate Schools." "The Crisis in Higher Education." "The PhD Rat Race." We can't afford to be complacent, Willett tells us.

We are under constant attack. But in the end we go on doing pretty much what we have always done. I might add, though, that our problem is made more complicated each year by passing time: since the classic days of scholarship (the old Harvard we can just remember) a whole new century has materialized. Those great old scholars were secure in their professional knowledge with no concern for the world of Joyce or Proust or Faulkner and their thousand disciples. When I was casting about for a dissertation topic back in the late twenties I fell upon a Victorian novelist named George Gissing, about whom little had been written, and I proposed to "do" him. But no, he was too recent, too "minor," perhaps too popular: certainly not a respectable topic for a thesis. Smollett, on the other hand, securely embalmed in the eighteenth century, belonged to the canon. My thesis on him, incidentally, turned up some good biographical material, and it is much to my discredit that I never made proper use of it. As I tell my students, year after year, there has never been an adequate biography of Smollett.

As for these accusations of shame and crisis that shout across headlines and magazine covers, I wish the glib critics could sit in on a few of Willett's committee meetings, or even follow through on the writing of a thesis, or attend an oral exam. Journals do thrive on accusations, and perhaps they stimulate more hopeful committee meetings and anxious self-inspections, but they become part of the general mindless griping about the world that afflicts us all. Some of our younger radicals, like Mortimer Finkel (he's the department assistant and poet whom Willett can't stand), assume that all human institutions are shameful—all, that is, except the utopian ones they are ready to die for. For a couple of years we had a novelist on our staff, a man who has since been cited here and abroad as an apostle of the "new novel," whose thesis (as far as I could make it out) is that nothing matters; all human effort is preposterous. His last novel ran to nearly eight hundred pages and his salary (at another university) is larger than any of ours. One of the targets of his mockery is the conventional scholar, the sedulous ant, as he calls him, the candidate for the PhD.

In the days when we were smaller and everything was simpler, I attended all the PhD orals. That was in the Partridge era, and he always presided like a professional master of ceremonies. He welcomed the candidate, told an appropriate funny story, quoted Mark Twain, all with an air of good fellowship among scholars and gentlemen. I must say that Willett carries on the tradition—he too is conspicuously a scholar and a gentleman; but the professorial panel is notably grimmer and more businesslike. Mark Twain is not quoted. The candidate sits in a straighter chair. And Jaeger and Grosbeck and Fulmar and McLoon make as formidable a set of grand inquisitors as one could possibly imagine. They aren't necessarily all there at the same time because now we have a committee system in order to divide the labor, as we are told—after all, an oral is a solid two-hour chore. (It used to be three-hour years ago, but strong men could barely endure it.) The committee system is also partly a way of selecting and eliminating certain members, and I am leading up to the fact that of late I have more often been eliminated. If I were to ask why, I'd be told that after so many years of service I was being spared a few of the extra chores, but I suppose the real reason is that I am not professionally sharp enough or tough enough to satisfy the younger men. Willett would tell me that I was of course welcome to come to any oral, as anyone of professorial rank is, but it is assumed that nobody wants to undergo such an ordeal unless he has to.

The candidate is attacked by specialists in various fields, but he is supposed to know everything. The game is a bit like poker; no one betrays himself. The questioners are in control, and can establish an attitude of imperturbable omniscience. "Suppose you begin, Mr. Linklater, by elucidating Grimm's Law." "You refer to the early liturgical plays as tropes, Mr. Linklater. Can you tell us what the word *trope* means, and why it is used in this connection?" "You mention Shakespeare's Dark Lady, Mr. Linklater. What is known about her? And how would a study of the Dark Lady sonnets contribute to an understanding of the plays? And which plays in particular, Mr. Linklater?"

The victim, sitting in a hard chair at the end of a conference table, must decide how far he can afford to bluff—and woe to him if his bluff is called, as usually it is. At some point he must show his hand. "What is Hotson's theory on the sonnets? Do you agree with it? And how about Schwankel's theory? Can you tell us about that? Have you read Brewer, Mr. Linklater?"

Very gentlemanly, of course. The victim admits that he has never heard of Schwankel, hasn't had a chance to look at Brewer yet, though he is aware that Hotson has some wild theories which are not considered sound by reliable scholars such as the ones now present. He, the victim, is in despair and would like to give up the game then and there, but he betrays as little as possible. He is stuck for another hour. He goes on with it.

Actually the Schwankel gambit is the sort of dirty trick Jaeger likes to play. He is probably an obscure German critic, untranslated, known to none of us except Jaeger, but we have to sit imperturbably and pretend that we know all about it.

If McLoon is on hand, however, the trick sometimes back-fires: "Who the hell is Schwankel?" he is apt to blurt out. "I never heard of him."

Our personal clashes are sometimes bitter, but they don't ordinarily flare out in public, as it were, or interfere with professional duty. McLoon is obviously an exception. And I suppose Jaeger is disliked by everyone. But his arrogance is effective and intimidating. He is a master of the dirty trick, and so far as I could ever tell he doesn't bluff—at least in his inquisitions. He has a prodigious memory and reads all the learned journals. He confounds any opposition by alluding to German or French sources. He sneers at everyone and everything, deplores the lack of scholarship among us, is ashamed of the paltry extent of our publications—though in the dozen years he has been with us he has published nothing more than a "note" on the possible implication of the title page of *Edwin Drood*. It is assumed (as it is for all of us) that he is at work on a scholarly production of a magnitude that will astonish us when it eventually appears, but except for the note on *Edwin Drood* we have no evidence of accomplishment.

Just last year, though, we had a pretty sharp set-to, with me in the middle, as it were. A man named Josef Mallick was taking his orals, and for a twenty-minute period it was my job to question him about the English novel. You'd think it would be a welcome subject, after the rigors of linguistics and Middle English and the rest, but in these times the novel is mostly neglected. There's no time for it, or perhaps it is too easy and pleasant a field for hard-driven students. They read a minimum sampling—one from each major novelist, many assume a superior attitude toward the old favorites, as though they no longer had any value for a modern intellectual. Any mention of Scott, for example, evokes a knowing smile—even though further questions discover nothing but ignorance about him. So Mallick and I groped along in search of a common ground and came to Dickens, where we paused to consider the relative comic effects of *Pickwick* and *Martin Chuzzlewit*. At this point Jaeger took over. It wasn't his business, really, but he was obviously impatient with our inconclusive discussion of comic values. Did Mr. Mallick consider Dickens a hypocrite?

It was a matter, we all realized, that Jaeger had strong views on.

Mallick, who had never thought of the question before, stumbled and stuttered. It was hard to say of anyone, he began—

What was Dickens's attitude toward sexual continence and marriage in his novels?

Mallick stumbled along, not unintelligently.

What about Dickens's own behavior?

Mallick mentioned new evidence—a mistress, actually . . .

Jaeger pounced. What is the evidence? What are the verifiable facts? Where are they to be found? Had Forster known about them? What does Johnson say? What does Marcus say?

Mallick by now was sunk. He could do nothing but gurgle.

I said, "Let's get back to the question of comedy and satire . . . ."

Jaeger said, "I want to get back to the question of Dickens's hypocrisy. Tell us, Mr. Mallick . . . ."

I suppose I do let people walk over me more than I should. It is a question, I tell myself, of whether the end is really worth fighting for—and more often than not it isn't.

Or so I reason. But something in Jaeger's tone of voice bothered me: he didn't really want to deal with Mallick as a student; he wanted to establish and dramatize his own attitudes toward Dickens. Not that I thought of all this literally at the moment, but I had realized for some time that Jaeger had a personal hatred of Dickens. As a matter of fact, his special "field" is Victorian literature, and so far as I can see he hates it all. He is convinced that they are pretty nasty hypocrites. But he uses Dickens as his chief target. Look at all the dirty stuff swept under the rug, he says. Look at the protestations of innocence and domestic virtue, and then consider the true facts of private life, the treatment of wife and children, the clandestine liaison with a young actress . . . .

He didn't say these things now, of course. But he often spoke of the "dark side" of the Victorian world, and suggested that such a book as *Edwin Drood* betrayed more pure evil than any of us realized. And in his pursuit of knowledge he evidently read deeply in the literature of what used to be called pornography—which he alluded to respectfully and clinically as the kind of source material a scholar had to absorb. I should add that he had a wife but no children; his wife was a stout, grim, Teutonic woman who looked ten years older than he. Our wits and cynics had a great deal to say about his private life.

I risked a protest. "I think my question had the floor," I said as politely as I could. "Perhaps satire does involve the question of personal intent, but I'd like to ask Mr. Mallick—"

Jaeger went on as though I were not speaking—and actually I don't think he heard me; he was too intent on his own purposes. "What can you tell us about Dickens's friend Collins?" he said. "Are there similarities in their behavior?"

Mallick was of course flustered, but he gamely tried to answer the more formidable question. There was something
about a woman in white, he recollected—and oh, yes, opium:
he thought maybe Collins took opium—

Why was opium so prevalent in the nineteenth century?
Were other writers influenced by it? The questions came at
such a rate that Mallick could do little more than stutter.
Had he read *My Secret Life*, by any chance? Had he read the
Carrington Letters?

Willett should have taken charge, but he was almost nodding. The room was stuffy. I tried to catch his eye. "I think
our time is running out, Mr. Chairman," I began with what I
knew was a hypocritical smile. I was quite angry.

But then Grosbeck took a hand. "All this concern for the
sins of the Victorians is irrelevant to our main purpose here.
It seems to me we are wasting valuable time—"

"It is not at all irrelevant," Jaeger broke in. "One of the
chief tasks of scholarship is to re-study the past in the light of
new evidence—"

"Gossip and pornography," Grosbeck began in a tone that
I recognized as very ominous—but by then Willett had come
to.

"Gentlemen," he said.

This had never happened in an oral before, at least so far
as I knew.

"I'm not concerned with gossip," Jaeger said. His emphasis
was emotional and righteous. "The truth is what it is,
whether you like it or not. There's no sense in trying to evade
it by calling it pornography."

Mallick, of course, said not a word.

Young Dunlin spoke up lightly, with his usual irony.
"Truth, as Pierre tells us, betrays us to pain—"

"Gentlemen," Willett said firmly. He was now alert and straight and looked every inch the varsity captain. "As Professor Sanderling reminds us, our time is indeed running out. Do you have any more questions for Mr. Mallick?"

Dunlin filled the somewhat embarrassed silence with a not-too-serious question about *Finnegans Wake*, which Mallick fielded deftly enough—it is always easy, as Dunlin says, to discuss *Finnegans Wake* even though you know nothing about it. The candidate was invited to step outside and await our verdict.

I may say at once that we passed him, more out of embarrassment at our own performance than respect for his ability. But Jaeger of course voted against him. He described him as one of the most incompetent men we had had in years—his ignorance of modern scholarship was appalling.

"I take it," Grosbeck said, "that by modern scholarship you mean chiefly researches into the private lives of the eminent Victorians."

"I mean honest research," Jaeger said angrily. "As for private lives, the phrase has no meaning. A life is a life. A man is what he is, whether he is a great writer or a nonentity. If he is worth studying at all, he must be studied truly. You can make fun of truth if you want to, but that's what our business is. If you try to evade it you are simply not competent."

Grosbeck, as I have said, was the most effective professional scholar in the department. He controlled his materials and applied his intelligence with what he and all of us recognized as supreme competence. Jaeger could have said nothing worse.

But you never knew how Grosbeck might react. Angus McLoon had called him a Nazi and brought down eloquent wrath and anathema upon his head—and of course it suggested a special vulnerability. But in the area of scholarship he probably felt himself to be impregnable. "I don't think I evade the truth, as you seem to imply. It is a pretty serious charge, actually—" He looked at Jaeger with an ominous solemnity, as though he were about to hurl a thunderbolt. But he didn't. "I have values," he said, making the words sound strangely eloquent. "Truth, as you rather glibly call it, is in itself without value. The human mind must judge and select. Facts can be trivial or irrelevant—or, as in the case of Dickens, used as a basis for slander or jealous attack. It may be that truth rightly used shall make you free, but there are truths that bind us in chains."

Professors as a rule are tactful enough not to lecture one another, but of course Grosbeck never bothered with ordinary amenities. He said what he said.

"I am so old-fashioned as to respect genius and believe in virtue," he went on, with a good deal of severity in his tone, as though he were addressing his pupils. "But I can assure you that I don't consider myself the kind of old-fashioned scholar who avoids unpleasant truths. If I choose to disagree with the Freudians, I do so on the basis of considerable knowledge."

This talk went on while we were presumably deciding on the fate of our candidate Mallick, who was waiting in a state of nervous exhaustion in another room. A few of the committee had already slipped out a side door. Willett was poised to step out and congratulate Mallick, which he could do with masterly grace, but he waited a little fearfully for the argument to run its course. He adopted an earnest smile for the occasion.

But Jaeger was very angry. He had acquired the habit of condemning his associates, and doing it with impunity; he hardly expected retaliation. You'd think he would be smart enough to keep clear of someone like Grosbeck, but for all his phenomenal memory he was not very smart—in his human dealings, at least. His arrogance had worked well for him, and he stuck with it.

He addressed Willett directly. "I protest at the sort of interruption I have been subjected to. It is highly improper on a formal oral examination for disputes and personalities to interrupt the questioning. It is, I believe, the function of the chairman to handle such matters." Before Willett could answer he turned to Grosbeck and went on. "As for your imputations about slander, I resent them. You talk of jealous attack, but it seems to me that that is exactly what is directed against me. Because you don't like my evidence you attack my motives. You are in fact building up what amounts to a conspiracy against me, and I assure you I won't stand for it."

Willett looked a bit scared, but he tried a hearty, common-sense approach. "Oh, come off it, Mark. No one is conspiring—the idea is preposterous. I'm sorry about the confusion on the exam—it was probably my fault, but I assumed that Sandy had the floor, as it were. Let's forget it anyway." He smiled. He looked very manly. "These are times that try men's souls, and I for one—"

Grosbeck broke in. "Some pretty harsh things have been said here. It is regrettable that we resort to personalities in our professional work. Difference of opinion is one thing, but since our task is primarily intellectual and critical—"

"Oh spare us the lectures, for heaven's sake. I think I know my duty as well as you do." Jaeger strode to the door. "I know how you feel about me too, and, as I said, I will not put up with it."

A vacuum of silence followed.

"He can make things difficult," Willett said with official politeness.

Grosbeck still looked very grim. His face was spotted with flush marks, and was somewhat white where his mouth had clamped itself. I had really expected him to lash out at Jaeger—I remembered his murderous anger when McLoon attacked him at the Medricks' party, but I could see that he was living up to his conception of professional responsibility. We were still concerned with the candidate, who still waited in the next room. "Jaeger's competence is certainly very great," he said. "His judgment, however, is questionable—in fact, I'm beginning to wonder if he is not somewhat paranoiac. If so, it is a pretty serious matter. His behavior to us and his attitude toward Mallick seemed at times irresponsible—even hysterical."

"Oh, I wouldn't say that," Willett put in, but his reaction was so characteristic of him that we hardly noticed. "Jaeger, like all of us, needs a rest."

Grosbeck looked at me. "I think Sanderling showed extraordinary forbearance and patience." Was his little smile touched with pity, or contempt? "After all," he went on, "he was inexcusably rude to you."

CHAPTER 11

PROFESSORS OF literature assume that they are privy to the secrets of human nature. They may themselves live in innocence, but they read all the revelations. Even if they restrain their more dangerous curiosities, they must in duty read the essential classics, from Aristophanes to Apuleius to Chaucer to Shakespeare. By the time they are old in the profession they know most of the folklore of sex and depravity. I remember the distinguished lady scholar from England who lectured on the sexual imagery of *Troilus and Cressida* in an almost impenetrable accent, while we listened with solemn professional attention. Now of course we have a school of writers who advocate sexual indulgence as the best thing in life, and they are being accepted and promoted in the academic world. Professors declare themselves against censorship of any kind, and appear in court in defense of *Fanny Hill* or *Lady Chatterley.*

But the truth is that I am not competent to reveal our secret lives—or perhaps I am reluctant, or simply afraid. With all my readings and observations, I live in isolation, like a hermit, remembering the ways of my youth when sin and virtue were as obvious as black and white. The idea of an open and proficient indulgence in sex just for the fun of it torments me with a kind of horror, even though I can appreciatively read about it in the pages of *The Golden Ass*. A department like ours, though, is a sounding board for gossip, and day after day we live in expectation of revealed secrets. Everyone, I assume, knew that Willett was once in love with Harriet, but since then layers of other rumors, false and true, have piled up. Whenever two or three are gathered together for talk, formal or informal, the question comes: "What's the dirt?"

It may sound mean, and as the plot stuff of stories and plays it always is mean, but the actuality is more often good natured and even magnanimous. We read Proust, or Balzac, or Shakespeare, and look with compassion on the desperations of celebrated characters: our own affairs in comparison seem modest. One of us may actually be a practicing homosexual, but he does the world no harm and is a competent scholar. We hear that Arthur Merlin has a "mistress" in town, and we use the classic word with a bit of ironic relish, realizing what a minor affair it probably is. We exchange imaginative jokes about Jaeger's private life, keeping in mind his grim and formidable wife and his Freudian obsession with the hypocrisies of the Victorians. There is a kind of folklore centering about McLoon and what it was that drove him to drink and destroyed his happiness—though he still lives with his wife and she takes care of him in his times of need.

These gossips come out at lunch, or at the beginning of a committee meeting when we are idly chatting. Teachers must lead a sort of goldfish-bowl life, and must learn to be discreet. Any man below the age of fifty (or even sixty) is in-

evitably a target for any number of female students—some of
them dangerous. Last year a likeable young instructor named
Horace Anser was fired because a girl accused him of seduc-
ing her—whether truly or falsely I can't tell. Anser was married, had two children, and chose not to defend himself—and
of course the matter was never made public: but I remember
the girl, a sweet, pretty, defenseless little creature—more
dangerous to a man than Circe herself.

Any university is full of them. They haunt the waiting
rooms and offices, they confer, seek advice, discuss—or they
assist, type, copy, file—or they lie casually in wait—or follow
you about—or leave little offerings on your desk—or write
perky notes. Among the hundreds who come and go are all
imaginable varieties of human female, and it is a commonplace to say that no man is safe. You can defend against the
predatory ones, or the calculating ones, or the wicked ones,
but not many men can withstand the wiles of high-minded
innocence. True love overrides all considerations—for a
while, at least.

It may be that I have provided gossip for my colleagues
over the years. I am susceptible to female attack. But actually, the most serious woman in my life, beside Harriet, was a
girl named Nora—and I still see her in a vision of love. Nora
Martin.

In my commutings between Newton and Harvard, back in
my student days, I found it easiest to walk (or run) the two
and a quarter miles to Watertown Square and take the
trolley from there to Harvard. Any other procedure was more
roundabout, and took longer. And I flattered myself that I
was getting in four and a half miles of daily road work—no
longer with any dream of glory on a track, but at least with
satisfaction in keeping up stamina and vigor. I could do the

whole route in under an hour—until I met Nora, that is. She took more time, but in the days of youth time is infinite.

She came and went on the car too, not always the same car, of course, but often enough for me to notice—and, to put the fact as candidly as possible, fall in love. As a reader of romances, I knew that some girls had divine attributes and Nora was clearly such a one. In externals she was as simple and modest as possible, but I saw that in her own secret world she was a princess and a heroine. She walked in a beauty of her own, untouched by the world of streetcars and traffic—as shy, I told myself, as a wild creature.

The world at large would hardly notice such a one—and of course in those days a modest girl made every effort to conceal herself. She wore grays and browns, skirts longer than fashion commanded (it was a short skirt era), no make-up, hair in a bun at the back—but to my eye she embodied all the visions of all the poets. I watched for her daily and weekly. I let cars go off, hoping she would appear in time for the next one. I noted her destination as Radcliffe—and even followed her through devious routes to where she lived in Newtonville, assuming in my folly that she was paying no attention to me.

It should be explained too that in those days there were pretty strict regulations about picking up a girl. I suppose Jaeger would point out that by tradition a picked-up girl was a prostitute, and the stigma was still very strong. It took me most of a year to figure out a way of properly "meeting" Miss Martin.

"You absolute ninny," she said later. "Why didn't you come up and say hello?" By then she had learned to speak affectionately, but it took a long time. As I remember, there were no such affairs as college socials, or mixers, where boys

and girls indiscriminately mingle: either you "knew" someone or you didn't. If you didn't know a girl, she looked
through you as though you weren't there. It seemed impossible to violate the social codes—in public view, at least.
When she said that to me—about my being a ninny—she
implied a sort of admiration: the code may have been preposterous, but I held to it. She herself was outwardly condi-
tioned to be a perfect lady.

The individual essence may be the same through life, but I
see the young Sanderling of forty years ago as though he were
a different creature—at least with a conscious critical effort I
can see him that way. At other times he becomes the "me" I
have to accept and live with. The sentimental dream is what
sets him apart. He yearned for love. He yearned specially for
a sweet shy maiden. All the songs and melodies represented
her, and all those fairy tales he had read from childhood on.
It was a pervasive and wondrous delusion, that world of
dreams, with the sweet songs always in the air—"Smiles," "A
Pretty Girl is Like a Melody," "Margie." I am not a wise
enough critic to say how much worse or better it was than
the present world, but I see my young self in a condition of
dangerous and pleasant innocence. Even the grief that followed had a quality or tone that made it seem worth living
through, like the sad breaking of hearts in the romantic
operas. The hero of Zenda lost his dream girl forever, but his
love sustained him. True love never failed.

Nora's mother was an invalid living in a great Victorian
house, dark under shade trees and dark with curtains and
blinds and heavy drapes and mahogany furniture—a wealthy
house in its day, with three floors, servants' rooms, pantries,
wine cellar, and a porte-cochere in front. I could hardly believe it when I first tracked her there, and I felt sadly un-

worthy of all that grandeur, but it carried out the princess motive that was already in my mind. This was no time for a hero to retreat. The Martins, I realized, had been very eminent indeed, and this was their castle—built of gray stone like all good castles. I had very glamorous thoughts about the maiden within.

It was some time before I realized that the maiden herself had arranged our formal meeting. Innocence of that kind is, as I've said, dangerous. There were connections through the churches, with meetings for young people, and conferences and delegations and other high-minded affairs, and in time I was introduced to Miss Martin who looked at me with polite indifference.

I say again that I loved her, then and there. She was blonde and white, with blue eyes—and she seemed almost transparent. A figurine of glass, slim and slight, with flows of faint color under her skin. Hair almost silvery in its paleness. She hardly noticed me, the water-blue eyes turned away, looked at others—but yes, she did go to Radcliffe—she did take the car at Watertown Square. The eyes returned with surprise—yes, of course she must have seen me on the car, now that I mentioned it. But how shy she was, how quiet and withdrawn, like a watching kitten. She volunteered nothing. She watched with a faint smile and a subdued brightness of face as though she were concealing feminine secrets. She waited—to be discovered, or reassured, or captured.

It took time, but the sequence seemed to occur inevitably, as though no other destiny were possible. As I stood beside her, struggling for the simplest banalities of speech, I felt the rush and whirl of true love. I was caught in a dizziness. I floated.

"You go to Radcliffe?"

"Yes."

"What class?"

"Oh, I'm only a sophomore."

"What are you taking?"

"Well—"

Slow work, but thrilling to a lover.

"Shakespeare with Kittredge."

"I hope I can have Lowes. They say he is retiring."

"Have you read *The Road to Xanadu?*"

"Have you read—?"

Nothing could stop the slow motion of our affair. We met on the streetcar and talked in a kind of basic conversational English. We walked—more and more we walked along miles of suburban streets. We sustained little jokes and pleasantries. We made a small dream world for ourselves. We thought we were getting to know each other—and perhaps she knew me better than I knew her: girls, I suppose, are shrewd; boys in love know nothing—at least they knew nothing in those innocent times. They are taught more realistically now.

I probably don't "know her" even now, but I can think about her more equably. I accept the fact that young Sandy was in love with her and never really ceased to be, though time swept him along to other ends. I see her still as the fair white princess in her gloomy castle, but the realities are sadder than I can fully understand.

She was reluctant at first to ask me to come into her house, and I thought it had something to do with the social grandeur of the Martins. I wasn't worthy of all that granite and mahogany. But in our daily walking and talking we were becoming inseparable—and I was filled with happiness and pride that she seemed to come to life when she was with me—she turned visibly pink and bright, and chattered along without self-consciousness. So she brought me into the house. "I must introduce you to Mother," she said.

It had to be arranged. There was tea in the large drawing room. Mrs. Martin in black, looking impossibly old and tired. Brown drapes with tassels at the windows, brown pictures on the shadowy walls, massive furniture half hidden in shadows. A servant creaked in with heavy silver—not exactly a servant, a housekeeper, a Mrs. Tupper, to whom I was introduced. She gave me a grim look.

Mrs. Martin made little effort to converse. She seemed too old to be Nora's mother but of course I couldn't tell. There was something very still about her. Nora filled the silences with bits of information about me and how we met, but I couldn't see that it mattered what she said.

After that we dropped in often, but Mrs. Martin seldom appeared—and the heavy silver and Mrs. Tupper didn't appear. The downstairs rooms seemed as empty as a closed museum. Not a sound or motion disturbed the air. There were "quarters" out in back somewhere, and a cook off in the depths—and no one else. A man looked after the grounds and did odd jobs, but lived elsewhere. A woman came in to clean, though I hardly ever saw her. The boss of the household was Mrs. Tupper, whose presence we always felt.

Nora tried to treat the place lightly and casually, but she did so with an effort. "It's really a mausoleum," she said, but the humor of it was not as light as she intended it to be. We used to sit in a little back room called the den—once a man's room, I gathered, with dark-green leather arm chairs and reading lights and a desk with a pipe rack and built-in shelves for books and curios—also a hand cranked phonograph and records. It could be the quietest place in the world, like the innermost chamber of a fortress. When we played the records, which we often did, the music seemed to sink into the heavy walls and carpets. I can still hear Caruso's pure tenor sounding in the dusky quiet, and the almost unbearable sweetness of Kreisler's violin.

But Nora's effort was always to be light and casual, as though all that weight of building and the gloom and silence were of no consequence. She behaved not like a princess under a spell, as I would have expected, but like a nice girl concerned with daily trivialities—she laughed and chattered along about whatever she saw and did. She avoided all sentiment and solemnity—for a long time, at least. We went to church socials together, we danced—with a good deal of humor at our awkwardness (though her grace and charm seemed perfect to me), we walked a great deal, we went to movies and concerts and galleries. I loved her and dreamed of our union, but for weeks and months we pretended nothing but respectful and light-hearted friendship.

What I loved specially in her was a sort of separateness from the world, a lack of the familiar contaminations. I suppose it was partly my dream of her as a princess apart, but actually she did lead a strangely separate life, with very few friends and relatives, and no desire for the ordinary social affairs. She never behaved like a rich girl or a sleeping beauty: she naturally enjoyed the plain and simple ways, and made fun of her own frugality. She wore rather shabby rubber-soled shoes and loose full skirts and sweaters she had knitted for herself—though of course in my eyes she always seemed exquisite.

Yet behind all this was mystery. The house itself was clearly dead. A mausoleum it almost literally was, and her jest came back to haunt me. Her mother, upstairs, living in

utter silence, seemed to be out of touch with mortal affairs—and though she must have been still in her fifties she
had the look of absolute age. Except for my visits, nothing
ever seemed to happen in the house—no callers, no relatives,
no sound of telephone or door bell. The basic services went
on as quietly as possible, with a minimum of outlay. I had
the impression that Nora barely got enough to eat, and when
we were out together, she hungrily downed hot dogs and
hamburgers and ice cream. Sometimes on a Sunday when the
cook was "out" and Mrs. Tupper was off duty she took me
into the vast cavern of their kitchen and assembled a little
supper for us—scrambled eggs and toast, perhaps, with milk.
The cupboards and ice box always seemed bare, as though no
one really used them. I found out later that their ordinary
meals consisted mostly of something on a tray—tea and
crackers and not much more.

A few fragments of rumor and gossip seemed to be taken
for granted in the community. Our little church socials were
pretty meagre events, but now and then I caught the name
Martin, spoken as though it belonged to the familiar
scene—like other notable names, Mrs. Jack Gardiner, for
one, or Lars Anderson or Amy Lowell. Some names seem to
hang in the air—you don't quite know who or what they
were, but you hear them, you remember the sound and
accent. Livingston Martin—was he an ambassador, a senator,
a cabinet member? He was something. He was rich. He
supported the Symphony, and the Museum of Art. His name
is in books. His portrait is somewhere. Was it his "den" we
retreated to? Was it there we agreed that we were in love?

But the rumors had a curious quality of melancholy: there
was something *about* the Martins, they were one of those old
families, they were rather odd—they were probably queer. I

never heard the accent of cruelty or jealousy, but rather of acceptance. It was taken for granted that the Martins represented a sad but familiar degeneration. What ever happened to young Lawrence? We used to see him. But they said his father had to be put away before the end.

Put away. That was the phrase. Sometimes people asked me. I saw Nora, I even "went with her," in the jargon of the time. What did I know about them? Did I ever see Uncle Weatherby? And Lawrence—he was such a good-looking boy—he used to go to the Fessenden School, didn't he?

I hardly wanted to ask her. The family and the house loomed too darkly. We played out our little duet with a deliberate frivolity—joking about her appetite and her frugality and her old shoes. But dammed up desire is great wherever it may be, and before I had taken any conscious resolution I was holding her on top of me in one of the big leather chairs. There is no doubt that we were compatible; we melted together with perfect ease and pleasure. But of course that was only the first step, the first breaking of the ice. We were full of guilt and fear and uncertainty about what to do next. All the social hazards and laws rose up about us. But that first time, for a few hours, was the purest and sweetest natural love: it is the time no one ever forgets.

From there on, though, the course of our love grew strange. My expectations were all derived from romantic readings, and I saw nothing ahead but happiness, with all the felicities of true love and of course matrimony; the problems of money and career would be met and solved as they came along. I had the flattering illusion that though I was poor, I was surely destined for modest success—specially in being appointed to rescue a princess from her dark captivity. And at first she clung to me with wonderful intensity; she burrowed against me, she held fast, she hid her face in my chest, she made inarticulate moans. But when I kissed her she grew radiant and laughed and came back for more, and we clung together.

Then, later, she cried—not loudly or openly, but with hidden intensity. She bowed her fair head down against me, curled up in a sort of protective tightness, refused to speak. She made emotional sounds, implying folly and frustration and unknown griefs. Then she came back to cling and be kissed, and smiled with tearful ecstasy.

I knew nothing about real women, and assumed that she was experiencing a normal emotional storm. She was wrought up—she was a girl of great sensibility. I watched her and handled her with extraordinary care and respect and a feeling of ownership. She was mine from now on. I was playing a part in a major drama. But as time went on, and we met and talked and loved, I felt her continually slipping out of my grasp. At times she was as frivolous as possible, almost frantically so; she teased me, sometimes to the edge of cruelty. She mocked my middle-class mediocrity, my play-safe timidities, and told me I'd better leave her alone, get out while I could. Then she said I was too good and too kind. Then she flung herself on me in an ecstasy. Then at other times she bemoaned her fate and herself, and wept, and hinted at mysteries and horrors.

We kept along with our daily rounds—walking, taking the car to Cambridge, doing our assignments. As a first-year graduate student I was bowed down with responsibility and a conviction of unworthiness, and spent many night hours trying to keep ahead of my work—and of course I slept too little and lived in a state of tension. She did bewilder me with her changes: she could work hard and well on her own assignments and then as likely as not push them all aside as not worth her effort. She had times of sober conscientiousness, even austerity, and noted how much time we wasted and how we diddled away our lives in selfish frivolity. She was angry with me for interfering with her life—and ruining my own, as she said. If I missed seeing her for some reason, she upbraided me.

But mainly she blamed herself. For a long time nothing was clear about it, except a basic emotional self-contempt. Everything was her fault. She knew better—had known better all along, from the very first. She was bad, wicked, *stupid* . . . .

When she was happy, in our love play, she glowed with color and brightness: she seemed to have all her heart could desire, and she became in all ways my heroine; I was continually rediscovering her story-book charm. But then she faded, drooped, sank into a deadly kind of sorrow that had no release. Whatever I did or said was of no avail—and sometimes I seized her and shook her in a fury of anguish.

I blamed her for being neurotic and self-indulgent. It seemed to me that any responsible person could surmount such fears and nightmares, specially Nora, who had so much of life and beauty and all the things we hope for. But when she did take thought and made the effort, as I might have put it, she almost frightened me with her intensities "Love me," she said. "Love me, love me, love me."

The family story came out, not quite all at once, but in sections. A taint of insanity, she called it, using old-fashioned language. Her grandfather may have been a great and famous man, but had I ever heard that he had deliberately cut off his left hand? It had once "stained his honor," as he had said. He was probably partly mad, but he could do great things.

Had I ever noticed that his portraits never showed his left hand? She had a memory of him in his age, and had always been frightened of him. Then—her father: a sweet and kindly man who had never "done" anything. Everyone said he took after his mother's family, the Havershams—he was delicate and somehow gifted, he should have been a musician, they said, or an "artist." But he had one of the proud names, and his father expected great deeds from him: the elder Martin, I gathered, lived a life of passionate pride—in his family, in himself and his abilities, and he naturally assumed that his son and heir would keep on with it. I think old Livingston was a brilliant and cultivated man, and if his son had succeeded in the arts, or in any reputable field, he would have been proud of him, but the fact seems to be that the boy—with the hopeful name of Bradley Haversham Martin—never had the energy to succeed at anything, though it must be said that Nora defended him and affirmed her love for him. Which in itself is a kind of success. Others spoke of him as nice but very shy. But he became an alcoholic, and he was finally put away. I never saw him.

Nora talked about them to me, but cryptically. She wanted to tell me. She insisted on being candid. But she dodged in and out of the truth as though she were playing with fire, ready to jest or weep or cry out, as the mood took her. She blamed, and praised, and despaired, and pretended to shrug it all off. "Grandfather," she said, "was a destructive force—he was like a hurricane. He couldn't help it, I suppose. But look at the wreckage—" She meant her father, of course, and her mother upstairs, and her brother.

That was the worst of it. Lawrence was only twenty-seven, but had never, as they said, "been right." He was in a private sanitarium, and much of the family income was being used to pay for him.

"So you see," she said lightly, as though it were a matter for irony, "I must never be a wife or a mother."

My life up to then had involved no such mysteries as these, and it took me some time even to be aware that they not only existed in reality, but had caught me in a web of trouble and danger. Even a young graduate student in the nineteen-twenties knew little of human abnormality. Insanity existed, one realized, and there were asylums and sanitariums, and doubtless there was a lot of expert knowledge among the doctors, but to innocent laymen like me it was all a matter of rumor, like wars in far countries. Hereditary taint—it was a fearful thought. The great house seemed to be an emblem of something hopeless and lost and sinister. Old families—people did somehow expect decay and disaster. But of course I couldn't believe any such fatality in my Nora, the girl who had somehow materialized out of my dreams. She was fresh and fair. We were together in body and soul. She was mine. The pact was made for life—or as lovers say, forever.

A kind of relentless movement took us along. Our secret life inevitably intensified, then changed. We were observed, of course. Mrs. Tupper frowned on us, and took it upon herself to scold Nora. The word got to Nora's mother. A slow and rather subterranean movement, a gathering of forces against us. The name of Uncle Weatherby was invoked—and presently he came for a visit and established a headquarters in the den. He lived in Arizona—where he had gone years before to cure a sinus infection—and devoted himself, as Nora explained, to the Grand Canyon. He took beautiful pictures, and had had an article in the *National Geographic*.

He also had charge of the Martin property—or at least

nominal charge: Nora sometimes referred to what "the bank" would or would not allow them to do, and I assume there was a trusteeship. Uncle Weatherby had a head-of-the-family status, and considered the big house as his own: he went about inspecting gutters and drain pipes and loose putty in the windows.

He never really "spoke to me." No one did, except Nora. But I felt criminally guilty, as though I were plotting to steal the silver. Uncle Weatherby was a nice man—I suppose he could be called an old-fashioned gentleman, very punctilious and nervous and fussy about little things, with a tenor voice and a high-pitched laugh, quite Bostonian in spite of his years in the west. But his fussiness could get very intense and sometimes almost hysterical, as when he found that squirrels had got into the attic and chewed up his "documents." Nora, of course, told me these things—with a kind of acceptance: her family were all queer, and there was no sense in being surprised at anything they did. No one knew what Uncle Weatherby's documents were, but he had stacks of stuff stored away in the house.

From then on, though, things changed. The year drew to an end. I had to make my utmost effort to get through my courses—and actually to my surprise I was awarded an MA degree and an assistantship for the following year. I was still "in."

But Nora—it is impossible for me to write in detail about her. My vision of her remained bright and clear—and has remained so ever since; she still exists in my eyes, the silvery light hair, the water-blue eyes, the faintly flushed clear skin, the slim girl's body, the mysterious entity of all of her together. I don't really know what it is that a man loves when he loves—I suppose often it is merely an idea and a dream.

But it has been part of my life for forty years.

After Uncle Weatherby's visit a relentless kind of finality set in. He had talked to her, of course. Her mother talked to her. Probably Mrs. Tupper did too. Up to then we had gone deeper into love and passion, and at times she had seized her moments with a strange and fierce recklessness. Afterward she faded, grew white and jumpy. We couldn't laugh about her appetite for hamburgers, or about her old shoes, or anything. She resisted love, turned cold and indifferent to all our play. No more walks, no outings and visits to museums. She sent me away, as she said, for the summer—it was "better" that way: she seemed almost hostile, as though I were doing her wrong. And actually I suppose I was. In late June she died. It was said she had a brain infection. But I think she took something—I don't know what. At the end, when I last went away, I could see the white misery of her face, but I couldn't believe what it meant.

✑ CHAPTER 12 ✎

MY CONCERN about a farewell speech is mostly a matter of vanity. The occasion is really a small one, and is soon forgotten. The good will is genuine enough, but certain conventions have to be observed—and a speech is one of them: or if not a speech, at least a few words, an acknowledgment of the monogrammed briefcase. It doesn't matter if you stumble and stutter—so long as you manage the little phrases of thanks and appreciation. And to tell the truth, most professors, for all their years of platform experience, are neither eloquent nor witty, though they try to be both. When the test comes I shall stumble and stutter with the worse of them, but meanwhile I compose charming spontaneous phrases—or perhaps wise ones, as I hope. Friends, colleagues . . . .

It is a game and some of it is pure nonsense. But you have to think in terms of a lifetime, a life's effort—and the coming of death. I can see it as "absurd," as some young philosophers are pleased to call it, but it is all we have. We do struggle and work, we do take things hard, we do live in hope. It all avails, we believe. This writing of mine is not very systematic and perhaps not even very serious in the conventional way of seriousness, but it really stems from my continuing rumination about what I can say to my colleagues and the world. What is it all for—particularly all this earnest scholarship, this "doctoral level" work we devote ourselves to? We actually deal with great numbers of students on all levels, fellow human beings, whom we coerce and influence. I'm sure we think about our efforts and intentions, but I'm afraid most of us let ourselves be carried along by the routine, like mules in a pack train.

And good scholarship may be enough in itself. It calls for accuracy and organization. It makes judgments and achieves new understandings. It has the warrant of respectable science, like paleontology or archeology—though at best it is more humanistic. Grosbeck's book on Thomas De Quincey is full of sound and accurate information and seems to me a sensible evaluation of the man, though it is much derided by the post-Freudian critics. But what I am getting at is my feeling (unfashionable, to be derided by nearly everyone) that out of deference to the scientists on one side of us, and the young nihilists on the other, we have given up any serious concern for moral good. Or moral beauty. Or simply beauty.

I am too much of a coward to say this literally. I couldn't say it, even in a farewell speech. "Oh, Robert Browning," they'd say. Or with contempt, "Tennyson." Well, I see that Tennyson's dream world is too far from the realities, as we understand them, but like old Partridge I admire Browning. People are always asking me to name "the five greatest English poets" and I always refuse to play their game, but I think of Browning. It does pigeon-hole me. It throws me back with my respectable old forebears who lived and died with the most literal notions of good and evil. They had no thought for the truth that went beyond both, or the form, or the beauty. My memory of Nora Martin was strangely unsettling to me and my ways: it seemed to add other factors or other dimensions to what I thought I had understood about life.

Her real name, by the way, was Eleanora. There is a stone with her full name on it in Mount Auburn, with other Martins. I don't actually go there and brood about love and loss; I could even admit, if taxed, that my love was a self-seeking and a gratification, but for forty years it has existed in my consciousness like a memory of music. When I was first aware of what had happened I wept painfully—with a sense of shame and guilt. But what are mortals to do?

My students tend to condemn all characters who get into trouble, and their major fault is weakness. Hamlet is weak. Macbeth is too, and Lear, and Othello. Stupidity is a form of weakness, and so is pig-headedness: look at Ahab, or Antigone, or Heathcliff. If they were doing it, the students, that is, they'd be shrewd and cagey and competent. They despise Emma Bovary not because she was a bad selfish girl but because she played her cards so stupidly. She let herself be vulnerable. She was weak.

One of my students (a phrase college teachers use with some unction) wrote a long analysis of the chief character in *Crime and Punishment*, also a student, Raskolnikoff, who felt that he was too valuable a man to be bound by ordinary moral restraints. He committed brutal murder as a way of advancing himself. And again the question was not as to the wrong inherent in murder, but the weakness and folly of the murderer. When we had a discussion about it I asked him—Stanley Weintraub, of Newark, New Jersey—what he thought about the moral issue, and he said it wasn't his business to take sides—he was merely observing and analyzing how it was done. Raskolnikoff failed, made a botch of the whole business; a stronger and more competent character might have succeeded. Dostoievski, of course, had a right to create a weak and foolish character—and he did it, Stanley was pleased to add, very brilliantly: but when such a character was used to point a universal moral, then one could question and even object. Dostoievski had a right to his moral philosophy but he had no right to stack his cards in order to demonstrate it. As to the crime—Stanley shrugged it off. Very messy, very *bad*, of course, but you can't generalize about such things. People commit crimes all the time—some worse than that: some suffer for it, some don't. You could write a great novel (he said) showing how a strong character might use such a crime as the stepping stone to success. Truth is truth, he said.

"You mean, whatever is, is right?"

"No, no—this rightness and wrongness business is irrelevant. Whatever is—*is*. That's what the artist needs to know."

You can see what a traditional character like me is up against. If I suggest to Stanley Weintraub that rightness does matter, is "relevant," he simply withdraws from me. He is polite enough, he doesn't strongly argue—he may shrug, not in arrogance but as a way of implying that the question is dead. Scientists deal with what is. Artists deal with what is. No one else in his world really counts.

We consider Stanley a very good student. He may be erratic in some of his grades because he is opinionated and he can be difficult, but we recognize him as one of us: he will go on through graduate school and be a formidable critic and scholar—not necessarily in literature. His kind of mind takes to the social sciences: he'll probably end up as an authority on the psychology of the artist.

It might be thought that in my professed concern for moral good I could think well of the passionate critics of our world and time, and of course there are a great many in and out of the classrooms. There are those who accuse Mark Twain of being a "racist" because the word nigger is used in *Huckleberry Finn*. There is a group led by one Mortimer Izzo who carry placards protesting the Christmas tree in the university plaza. There are always a few who are ready to walk out of commencement exercises if they disapprove of the politics of the speaker. And there is constant guerilla warfare on the question of the control and censorship of student publications. It is unfair to generalize about them or lump them together—except to say that my own temper dislikes agitation or militancy (I remember how Nora Martin sometimes mocked me for my cowardice). But I signed an anti-war manifesto once—perhaps I did it for Nora. That's about as far as I could ever go. The dedicated reformers are really too self-righteous for me.

Except for this Mortimer Izzo: he was another one of my students, and I decided in the end that he simply had a screw loose. He was crazy. But he was a very sweet and beguiling youth with a dark eastern look to him and opaque eyes and a ready smile. He did everything carefully and literally—his work as a student and as one dedicated to the elimination from public life of all religious observance and superstition. "It is merely a bondage, like chains," he said, smiling with white teeth as though he were delighted with a joke of some sort. "It is outlawed by our Constitution," he said. When I tried to point out that a Chrismas tree was merely part of a cheerful festival that everyone could enjoy he smiled brilliantly. The birth of Christ, he said, had led to centuries of persecution and war and misery. It was not good to commemorate it. He was not jealous for other religions, as many were—he was neither a Mohammedan nor a Hindu nor a Jew; he was a free man, and he wanted all Americans to be free men too. He had followers—they were a little group, but growing steadily. Perhaps I would like to join, or even contribute a little something?

It doesn't seem to me, as I now think of it, that I can possibly speak seriously to my colleagues about our aims. My program, if any, would be simply a re-stating of all the too-familiar values: the use of reason, restraint, common sense, common decency, common honesty, the effort to be patient and as brave as possible in accepting what must be, the effort to do things well and beautifully. It is what you used to hear in small-town commencement addresses; it is not the thing to say to philosophers and intellectuals. And though it is really the only program in life I can subscribe to, as it were, I have the uneasy feeling that it is all much too naïve. The critics who write for the intellectual journals (some of my colleagues among them) are arrogant in their certainty that man's spiritual and psychic problems are insoluble. To all who inhabit the earth today, whether they think or feel, life must be a tragedy.

So I keep rather quiet about it.

I try to learn—or at least to watch and understand.

A few years ago a girl named Judith Samaris came to see me about her course work—she asked me to sign a form of some sort, which I did. She was one of a class of fifty, and I hadn't known her name. She stood by my desk while I signed the card. "How are things going?" I asked.

"You like those novels you talk about, don't you?"

"Like them?"

"Smollett and all those—I never read them before."

"Well, yes—I suppose I like them."

"I think I do too—some of them, anyway. Have you ever read *Fanny Hill?*"

I waited a moment. "Yes," I said.

She sat down.

You may remember that the book is a glamorous and eloquent account of the doings of a London prostitute. It was written two centuries ago and was intended as pornography. It is now being praised for its art and truth, and I assumed that young Miss Samaris was probing to see if her professor was up to date in his values. I looked for that little twist of cynical arrogance that some of the bright ones adopt when they challenge their teachers.

But all I saw was a relaxed and placid young female. Dark cloudy hair, white skin, small nose, big eyes and mouth, long legs, and an air of patience as though passing time had no significance for her. No special smile, no little way of calling attention to herself. She sat there.

"Can I talk to you?"

It was not shyness, but there was a good deal of doubt in her voice.

I said yes, of course, and there was a long silence. Then she pulled herself together. "I guess—some other time, if it's all right with you. I'm not sure what I want to say."

"Are you having trouble?"

Her smile was astonishing. My response to attractive girls is probably normal—and men in their fifties are as responsive as they ever were. I could feel myself quiver inside. Her mouth and eyes seemed wonderful to me.

"Trouble," she said quietly. "I don't know. That's probably it—I don't know. You are married, aren't you?"

I nodded.

"How old would you say I am?"

"Oh—nineteen, twenty."

"Twenty-six," she said.

"You've probably got it wrong."

"No—I'm sure about that, at least." She stood and moved to the door. "Can I come in again? I really would like to talk to you—I think I would, anyway. Not now—but sometime . . . ."

It was a month or more before she came again. She made a little excuse to consult me about a paper she was writing. I was by then very conscious of her, of course—and watched her coming and going in the classroom. She had a quiet air about her, was graceful and slow in her motions; she never seemed to have to do with others—no chat or exchange of greetings. She generally got B-plus grades: she was competent, but lacked the background of the best students.

"I like all this literature," she said, "but it is sort of frightening."

"Why? Why frightening?"

"Oh—well, there's so much sin."

I tried to laugh it off. "Sin seems to make the best drama."

"It's all supposed to be true, isn't it? I mean you talk about these things—" She groped for her words and fell silent. "It's the way people have thought for hundreds of years. Hundreds and hundreds. We had to read Greek things—plays. And Shakespeare. And American lit—"

"Not all," I said hopefully.

"It's what you take seriously, isn't it? I mean the profs all do. We're all supposed to."

Groping. She wasn't attacking. She was searching for something.

"They all die young—pretty young, anyway; or they live in misery. What I mean is, they are punished. Is it supposed to be God who does it?"

She wouldn't pin me down as some do. She seemed to expect to do her groping alone, but she had more on her mind than she knew what to do about. She didn't ask me if I "believed" in this or that, or if I could solve her problems. There was something oblique about her, perhaps cagey, though she spoke quite literally. "I guess I like these novels we read—people like Fielding and Smollett—because they don't seem to worry. They just—live, the people like Tom Jones and all—"

"They have standards," I said.

"Well—of course, they try to be kind, the good ones, I mean, and generous and honest. I bet Fielding was that way—I bet he was a wonderful man. But they don't worry about their souls, or about guilt, or committing unforgivable sins."

It was another couple of weeks before she came in again. This time she gave me the wide glowing smile, like an old friend. I did feel magnetized by her with the current that mysteriously jumps between a woman and a man—very rarely with me, I must say. But her smile shot right into my timbers, as Smollett might put it.

"I need to talk a little again," she said. "Can I—or would you rather I came some other time? It is not really anything vital, I guess. I mean, I'm not very important—"

The idea of going out with her stirred in me. It was wintry, not a time for strolling in a park or sitting on a bench. The usual thing was coffee, but the places were noisy and smoky. I tried to see what it was about her that magnetized me. Her body was no different from hundreds of others that came and went, and her face was attractive enough, as we say, but not the sort to win beauty contests. She hadn't really said very much, but she had a modesty and candor of speech that I liked. And of course her smile was like a sudden flash of sunlight. She seemed exceptionally clean too—though I realized that girls were all exceptionally clean these days. Perhaps it was her quietness. Or the slow way she moved, or simply the rhythm of her body.

My office was a quiet place, with books and a rug and some Hogarth prints on the walls. A spot of river was visible from the window, now icy and remote.

It was up to me to begin. I was afraid she would get up and go again. I asked her what she wanted to do after she graduated. Would she teach?

"You know I have a little girl," she said. "She's six."

"I don't really know anything about you," I said. It wouldn't do to ask about her husband, I thought—and then realized I was being foolish. She had troubles, she had come hoping to be able to talk. She probably wanted me to ask.

"I've never been married," she said.

That was it, of course. She brooded and worried. She read plays and novels about all the sinners who came to grief.

I was filled with compassion—and regret. The regret was simply a physiological twinge, and seemed absurd to me. Whether she was a virgin or not had nothing to do with me, and never would. I took note of how beautifully fresh and clean she was and allowed myself some ironic reflections on the predicaments of sex. She was obviously a nice sensitive girl with good intentions.

"When I was thirteen," she said, "my family was killed in a crash—I mean my parents and my brother: we were driving back from New Hampshire and a car came right across the dividing strip—right into us." She spoke a bit remotely, as though she were not concerned with the emotional connotations. "I was banged up—I came to in the ambulance on the way to a hospital—but I survived. They said I'd be as good as ever—" She let the words hang for a moment. "But of course life, my life, has never been—I mean it has been pretty strange—"

She was still detached, but I had a sense of vast nameless troubles. Whatever had happened to her since then must be to her credit.

She lived for a while with her uncle's family in Somerville but they considered her a burden. Her mother's parents in Waltham took her in, and she went to high school there —but they were old and strict: her grandfather Bragdon had been a science teacher in junior high school and was an old-time martinet—not that she used that term, but I could picture him as a dogmatic disciplinarian. She suffered and brooded and ran away. She got into trouble. I built up a drama in my mind. She was betrayed and abandoned.

I wondered what she lived on. Some small inheritance, perhaps. Insurance money—compensation from the accident: you read of such things. "Have you been working?" I said. "Have you had a job?"

"Well—" She sat quiet for several seconds. "In a way—" Then she stood up and gathered her books and handbag. "It's foolish to do all this worrying. I'm usually pretty good at letting things happen. But having a little girl to bring up—and then reading all this stuff and hearing people argue about it—" She smiled with a touch of apology. "I can't seem to discuss very well, the way some of the kids do. I'm in one course where they all go on about people I never used to

know existed—I mean like Sartre and the rest—one boy
keeps wanting to read William Burroughs. I mean he wants
to read him aloud. I suppose you know all about him and
these others."

She treated me, I realized, as an oracle. She assumed that I
knew everything.

"I don't really like them," she said. "They're kind of dirty,
don't you think? I mean real dirt, the kind you have to wash
off. But in some ways I feel—" She broke off. "I've got to go.
Can I come back later?"

Again that odd skittishness. She reminded me of a young
cat that had been left in the woods by lumbermen—we
found it up near Stafford Mountain once when we went
trout fishing years ago. It wanted to be taken care of in the
way of cats but it wanted to stay free and wild too. I don't
really know why she took to me, except that she enjoyed
those eighteenth century novels and she seemed to think I was
a sort of sponsor for them. She kept coming back, always
apologizing for taking up my valuable time. She was respectful—too much so: I didn't fancy my rôle as oracle. But
underneath that, or aside from it, she could be shrewd and
ribald and sometimes funny—mostly at the expense of my
colleagues. She could chatter along, with gossip and anecdote; she could give what she called a girl's-eye view of faculty affairs. Our dean, for example, was an ex-clergyman of
very serious moral and intellectual intentions, but he was a
compulsive girl-patter. "Next time there's a party, you watch
his hands," she said. "He pretends he doesn't know what they
are doing." When I asked if they objected—the girls, that is,
she turned on her smile. "Most of them love it. They think
he's nice. But it all depends, of course. You can't stand being
touched by some men—I don't know why. That's really what

bothers me—I mean—"

"What bothers you?" I asked.

I had been trying to get at this, of course. We were by now friends, in a sense. She called me Sanderling—nothing else. The kids all call their profs by their last names, she explained, and it seemed normal.

"You've been brooding about something ever since you came to see me—weeks ago."

"I know," she said quickly.

But the more friendly she was, the more evasive she seemed. "It isn't right to take your time this way," she said.

But of course there had been hints. Fanny Hill—we had started with her. I began to put things together. She couldn't really tell me, but she wanted me to dig it out of her. What is sin, she asked.

Well, it came as a shock to me. I knew in the abstract, as we all do, that young people were devoting themselves more and more to sexual activity, and were talking about it with arrogance or vanity, but to realize that my new friend had been making her living out of sex for nearly ten years was at first more than I could adjust myself to. This sweet clean creature, full of gentle consideration and responsive humor, actually took off her clothes and copulated. For money. Professionally. I groped among the possibilities. Ten dollars? Fifty? Night after night—with strangers? A manager, perhaps. Call girl—that phrase came glibly.

"I guess you are horrified," she said, with an odd little touch of anguish.

The fact is that I loved her. I had a wonderful sense of her magnetism. Hundreds of girls came and went in our rooms, and now and then I felt the strong sexual pull that is beyond any explanation, but with this girl, Judith Samaris, the force surrounded us like an electric charge. She often wore dresses without sleeves, and her white arms seemed to be there for me alone.

"Well," I said, concealing as much as I could, "it's not something I know very much about."

A lame remark. I almost choked over it.

Her mouth, without make-up, was large and sweet, with the oddest look of irony as though it were on the verge of uttering the exact right word. But now it had softened into anxiety, and her dark-brown eyes were liquid. Could she be crying?

"It wasn't fair of me," she said. "I just thought I'd talk to someone—a wise professor, like you. I've enjoyed—I mean I've *liked*—" She stopped. "You know what I mean."

It was obvious. I thought if I were twenty years younger I'd have her in my arms. I thought nothing would matter—nothing else, that is.

But—all those men. I thought of the men—and her. It was ridiculous, of course. Old professors are always getting into predicaments like this.

College was a big experience for her, she said. History and lit and philosophy and art—she loved it, she got more out of it than the young kids. But trying to *think* nearly drove her crazy. She'd had a course in Dante, but why would anyone take Dante seriously—why all this agony about hell and punishment?

It was her life, I told myself. Her business. I couldn't touch her—not very much, anyway. I looked at her expressive mouth. Did all her men see what I saw? The effect of shock was still strong in me.

"I don't let myself worry," she said. "I try not to. But I guess I do, even so. Grandfather used to pray for my soul. I tell myself I don't have a soul. But you can see I wanted someone to talk to." She smiled so glowingly that I lost my bearings, I sat there in a slowly swimming cloud.

"Do you want advice? Comfort? Wisdom?" I spoke a little sharply, with a professional sort of sound. No betrayal, I thought. Old prof is not about to make a fool of himself.

But she laughed it off. There was no one she could talk to, she said. The people she knew didn't go in for that sort of thing (did she look at me with irony when she said that?), and she didn't see much of her fellow students. If she went to graduate school, of course, she might get to know some of the older ones—

"Graduate school?"

"Do you think I could? Would I be foolish to try?"

No bearings yet. You think you know all the possibilities in life and then you meet Judith Samaris.

"I have a good record, you know."

I managed to chuckle at that, but for once she didn't respond.

"Yes, I do want advice. Never mind the comfort—or even the wisdom, though I can always use some. But I have to bring up my daughter, I have to live, I have to grow old."

I thought of taking care of her in some magic way—in a cottage with flowers, perhaps.

"Is it guilt that bothers you?" I blurted out. It was a crude question; I hadn't intended to ask it.

But she was resolved to treat me respectfully. She considered seriously. "I guess it is. In terms of my little girl, and any sort of life I might try to plan. The long run I mean. You don't think about that at first." Her face set itself in odd wrinkles of anguish. "You know, all I did for a while was *hate*—I hated my grandfather. He made everything seem guilty. I didn't care what I did. I went with a fellow just to get away—and after that—"

She talked, but somehow never got to the point. The familiar miseries of love, desire, poverty, the fevers of youth, the strategies of survival—all leading to nothing but accumulated futility. It is recorded, over and over. I felt her anguish, I even felt a gnawing grief of my own that I hadn't been able to rescue her. I conceived of a world of beauty and delight in which she might have existed.

But the *point*—it was really the mystery, the meaning, the truth of all that sexual activity. That's what I couldn't grasp. I wanted to ask her: what? what? what?—but there was no way of framing the question, and though she if anyone could answer the unframed question, there was really no answer to it. She sat there relaxed in her lovely sex, hair shining, face scrubbed, arms and long legs gracefully disposed, full of respect for me, and candor and good will and a kind of charming humility, yet she could never reveal the true secret. In a way she herself was the secret—or the emblem of it.

"The terrible thing," she said, "is that you don't care. You don't care about anything. You don't win or lose or get anywhere—except from one day to another. That's the way it was for me for a long time, and the people I used to see. Maybe that's what sin really is."

"But you do care?"

"Well, I get to wondering about my child. I'd just like to take her out of all this. Isn't that a good idea? Wouldn't you do it if you were me?"

I agreed, of course. She smiled gratefully, as though I had done something magnanimous. "It's nice to have a friend here," she said. She said it respectfully. Humble student to old prof.

"What do you think of *Fanny Hill?*" I asked.

"Oh, it's very phoney. Clever, I guess; it sounds good. But believe me—" She gestured with disgust.

"Why don't you rewrite it?"

She eyed me, almost with suspicion, then shrugged. "The woods are full of real Fanny Hills. It isn't what I'd want to write about—or could. The truth is pretty old and dreary stuff." Then she smiled in recollection. "But that Henry Fielding—he's the one I go for."

No lingering agonies in Fielding, I gathered. No psychological hell. You did wrong, you got slapped down by law and virtue, and that was that. You certainly didn't suffer through life with a scarlet letter on your breast. I saw her point.

In that class of fifty there was only one Judith Samaris, but each day as I looked them over I wondered. The human woods were full of strange creatures, and here they were, the clean and nubile females, the males mostly uncouth and sloppy—but predatory and potent. The secret would never be revealed, I supposed.

ᴥᏕ CHAPTER 13 ᏸᴥ

A WEEK OR SO after the notorious Mendrick party I had a note from Professor Grosbeck, typed on memorandum paper and signed with a scrawl of initials. He hoped I'd be free for a few minutes at two-thirty the next afternoon, after my class. He had looked up my schedule, I realized.

He did things in a formidable way, and I braced myself to withstand him. I reviewed my more recent failings—the down-town walk for example, or the habit of bed-time murders which had lately been taking up more and more of my evenings. As far as I knew, he had no failings. It astonished me that he would give up even a few minutes of afternoon time in order to pay me a visit, and I speculated about it a bit fearfully. He did have very strong opinions on political and social questions, and I wondered if he intended to enlist me in a cause or get me to sign a manifesto or be on a committee. He wouldn't be consulting me about scholarly matters, I was sure. He was writing what we understood was to be the definitive history of romantic transcendentalism, and of course I could have nothing to contribute to that. I saw my whole pleasant and trivial life in graphic contrast to his daily and hourly achievements.

Ordinarily, I had very little to do with him. Department meetings, PhD orals: otherwise he was preoccupied in the manner of high officials and great men. An occasional small dinner, though. He had a wife of delicate health, a lady much admired for her southern sensibility and charm, who never went to big parties: she and Harriet did not get on well together, but now and then we met at someone's house—it was the Fulmars who occasionally asked us, though I don't know why. Fulmar was the kind of conservative and respectable scholar who fitted well with Grosbeck, but I felt like something of an impostor.

He came in on the dot, briskly, without hesitation. A human engine, I thought. Chunky of build, but not much belly—not to notice, anyway. A tailor-made suit—at least it seemed more opulent than most suits—a brown mixture of hard-twisted wool. Perhaps ready-made stuff wouldn't fit him, or perhaps he figured that if a tailor once got the measurements right he could turn out a duplicate whenever it was needed. Anyway, he did look well upholstered—not elegant in the Willett manner, but nonetheless expensive. His was not the varsity effect, of course. He had a squarish outline—perhaps even a Teutonic one, with steel-gray hair flat on top, broad low forehead, very broad jaw, even a broad (as well as large) nose. The mouth, soft and rather expressive ("weak," some of my students would be bound to call it), seemed out of place against the granitelike cut of the face and head. It was impossible not to see him as a Germanic type, a herr-professor of the old regime, an academic staff-officer. You half expected him to issue formal commands like an actor in a war melodrama.

But of course all that was mere delusion. I had been corrupted by McLoon's drunken prejudice. He spoke with gentle cordiality. "Sanderling, how are you? What are you up to these days? We should get together more . . . ." We shook hands (a continental mannerism?), we smiled, we inquired for wives and families—he had a son who was already famous as an astro-physicist.

But the cordiality did seem surprising to me. His smile was almost effusive; I noted that he held it with an effort—he even squeezed my hand with a sort of lingering effort.

This was a busy hour of the day, he knew, and it was kind of me to make time for him—he went on with these formal preliminaries for several minutes, then sat down in my visitor's chair, then glanced right and left through his thick lenses as though he suspected eavesdroppers in the corners, then got to the point—or at least began moving in the direction of the point.

I had been at the Medricks' party, he noted. A very *unfortunate* party—a touch of pink showed at his temples as he spoke, but it was evident that he meant to be cool and judicious. "I have been attacked in the past," he said reasonably, "on various grounds, critical and philosophical, but I have never before been subjected to personal vilification like that. It came as an extraordinary shock, of course. I was angrier than I have ever been in my life."

He spoke as one drawing up a report, glancing as he did so at me to make sure I recognized the justice of his conclusions. He tried to allow for the fact that McLoon had been drinking, but of course drunkenness, etc. His observations were predictable, but restrained.

I was naturally embarrassed to be once more involved in all this. I could nod now and then at the effective truths he delivered. I could frame a cliché or two in my mind, I could mumble a few thoughtful affirmatives, but for a time it all seemed oddly unreal, and I wondered what had got into the supremely competent Professor Grosbeck. What was he getting at? And why me?

Well, he had a letter—from McLoon. He unfolded it, looked at it in bewilderment. He thought perhaps I might advise him; he valued my judgment, he respected my something-or-other . . . .

So. I may have glanced into the corners to look for eavesdroppers or to make sure he was not talking to someone else. But he fixed me with a pale blue gaze, and that unexpectedly soft mouth actually expressed anxiety or uncertainty or some feeling not suited to a man of strong decision.

It does happen now and then: a student, a layman, an outsider, will respectfully ask for an opinion, philosophical or literary or even political or social. Professor, what do you think of Albee as a playwright? What do you think of the policies of the School Committee? What's your attitude toward the draft, or short skirts? Is *Lolita* a great novel? But of course my colleagues don't ask me such questions, and the last one I should ever have expected to is Grosbeck.

I sat up in my chair. I could feel myself taking on solemnity and responsible wisdom, like a very large and cautious owl. Somehow I had to come up with an answer appropriate to the occasion. He valued my judgment.

But first the letter.

"Dear Grosbeck: My memory of events at the Medricks' party is not clear, but I am convinced that I behaved inexcusably. It may be of some small satisfaction to you to know that I dwell in disgrace and folly, that I am a pariah, that decent society abominates me, that your opinion of me, as expressed eloquently and cogently and memorably, is if any-thing too kindly. I write this in apology. Self-pity, in a person of my depths of failure, is contemptible. Excuses are frivo-lous. Expectation of mercy is vain. Judgment has long since been rendered, and punishment is in process. Yours sin-cerely."

I may not give it accurately, but it made quite an impres-sion on me. Perhaps it was even more emphatic than my re-production here. I read it twice—perhaps thrice.

"He has quite a style," I said with what I hoped was a light touch of appreciation.

"Style?" Grosbeck said sharply.

As I have noted, he had very little of what we call a sense of humor, or of irony. And I uneasily recognized my own tendency to be frivolous, or perhaps evasive.

"Well, his letter is a—a composition." It seemed a lame thing to say, but actually I was fascinated by the letter. I read it again.

"The question, I should think, is not one of style, but of human relations. How am I to answer such a letter?"

This called for the appropriate answer. I thought grop-ingly. Once upon a time it might have been pistols at twenty paces. Or swords? A frivolous notion.

"Perhaps you don't need to answer it," I said very tenta-tively.

He did me the honor of considering the suggestion seri-ously.

"The apology is handsome enough," he said. "Do you pro-pose that I merely accept it and hope that the matter will be forgotten?"

I didn't like that "do you propose" gambit. I squirmed a little. "May it not be forgotten?" I said.

He had been thinking a good deal about the problem, and his response was strongly phrased. "Allegations have been made, slander has been uttered. My reputation as a responsible citizen and scholar has been attacked—it has in fact been attacked so crudely and brutally that I have suffered what amounts to a shock. I have even considered the possibility of redress at law, since the attack occurred in the presence of a large company, but the only attorney I consulted advised me strongly against it. He felt, apparently as you do, that the matter could well be forgotten. A lawsuit, he said, would lead to uncontrolled notoriety. But nonetheless, my good name is precious to me. I am not content to let the whole thing drop. But I am not at all sure what my next move should be."

He eyed me expectantly. I thought as quickly as I could and said nothing.

"You are a just man," he said with an embarrassing amount of resonance, as though the pronouncement were somehow official and almost ecclesiastical. "I have spoken to no one else, but I would value your opinion. It would seem to me that Willett should have taken some action, but I know that his only concern is for surface appearances—" I could feel the edge of contempt in his words, though he still spoke with a sort of official accent of truth. He assumed that all just men knew that Willett's only concern was for surface appearance. "I hesitate to bring the matter to the attention of the administration, though I am sure the president would be seriously concerned, and might want to take action. But I shall avoid recrimination and proliferation . . . ."

I did feel like a serious and silent owl. I realized how very important some people were. Recrimination and proliferation—you can't say words like that without knowing that

your self and all your affairs are matters of extreme significance in the world. I had one of those odd flashes of memory: there was a lady in the Newton of my youth who lived
in a mansion with a retinue—I saw in my mind the gravelled
drive, the Rolls Royce, the liveried chauffeur, and my young
self in short pants chasing a ball that had rolled almost all
the way along to the front door. "And who are you?" she
said, stepping out of the tonneau shrouded in filmy veils with
an immense hat with birds on it. When I mumbled my
name she told me to speak up clearly, which I didn't succeed
in doing. "Well, I am Miss Bissell, and I don't allow little
boys to run on my driveway. Be off with you!" She did smile
a little, but it glittered. She turned away. I felt the eyes of
the chauffeur on me in my retreat. She had another mansion,
they said, at Bar Harbor.

"We live," said Grosbeck, "in a time of virulent partisan-
ship. Vilification and accusation are the weapons of a new
barbarianism—even among men who are presumably scholars
and responsible thinkers."

Miss Bissell, we were told, had inherited woolen mills.
"Tell Michael," she said to the chauffeur, "to see that the
gates are kept shut." But I had no resentment against her, or
class jealousy; no reflections about social imbalance occurred
to me then or later. She was a fact of life, a personage of
mysterious importance, like a queen. I suppose there's not
much point in alluding to her, except that the little vision of
that scene did come back to me as Grosbeck talked.

"I realize that I am to be considered a conservative," he
said. "I advocate responsible leadership. I deplore the moral
and social anarchy of our so-called liberals, who seem to feel
that good can be achieved without discipline or order. It is a
sentimentality so dangerous as to be criminal."

Again I could only mumble and try to look judicious. As a man-in-the-middle on all these grave questions I can make no firm statements. Grosbeck was of course quite right. He had no doubt whatever about his rightness. But half the young men in our department would have been outraged at his opinions and his attitude. They would be right too. Their rightness would be more appealing than Grosbeck's.

"As to this letter," he went on, as though it were all the same argument, "I feel that I cannot simply let the matter rest there. Serious damage has been done, my reputation has been publicly traduced . . . ."

He certainly couldn't let it rest. He was obsessed by it.

"I find this letter unpleasantly arrogant," he said. "The man is concerned only with his own personal catastrophe. His apology is like a boast, an almost complacent display of his tragic plight—and perhaps at another time, under other circumstances, I might regard the matter with some detachment. You could conceive of McLoon as a protagonist in a medieval moral tragedy. You admire the *style* of his letter, and I have no doubt that he congratulated himself as he wrote it. But my own problem is still unsolved."

If there were a duel, I'd be his second. I would make formal representations to McLoon—or would he have a second too? I repressed the least twitch of lip. I coughed. My principal insists on a public retraction of these slanders . . . ."

"I gather," he said rather sternly, "that you would advise me to take no further action."

"Well, I probably wouldn't," I said. "But taking no action is my solution to most problems. I certainly don't expect others to behave as I do." I again repressed any twitch of a smile—it was no time for frivolity; but I realized that what I said was not really serious, or adequate.

But he took earnest note of my remark. "Yours is doubt-less a more purely Christian attitude." He said this very thoughtfully. "I will take it into consideration. I am grateful to you for your interest. I would hesitate to impose on most of my colleagues in this matter, but I knew I could count on your good will and judgment. I myself am not so purely a Christian. I cannot agree to the doctrine of turning the other cheek—again, it seems to me to lead to a dangerous senti-mentality. But in such a man as you, the ideal may be seen as noble."

By this time I was squirming with embarrassment. "No, no," I said. "I haven't any theory. I just hope that troubles will somehow go away." I didn't quote McLoon's remark about "thinking little" but I remembered it. "You have every right to refute slander," I went on. "But my idea is simply that you don't need to. Your work, your accomplishments, your character, are too well known and understood . . . ."

I actually said that. I could feel a flush on my face. Was I piling it on? There were those who really agreed with McLoon, not so emphatically, perhaps, but I had often heard the phrase "fascistic thinking" used in reference to Grosbeck. "Right wing" too. "The extreme conservative position."

"You really have no need to vindicate yourself," I said again. But I did feel a little twinge of hypocrisy. Couldn't he really stand a good deal of vindication? "The effort might simply—" I waved a hand a bit vaguely. I had almost said that it would simply stir up trouble, but it struck me that he was in a way looking for trouble. "It might lead to notori-ety," I said.

He nodded—always with judicious gravity. His powerful mind was at work on the problem. "The wrong kind of noto-riety would indeed be deplorable—when you think of what our irresponsible journalism can do these days. And as you say, my work is pretty well known—" He nodded with detachment.

"What I suggest," I said impulsively, "is that you simply let some of our colleagues see this note. I'm sure Mac intended it to be seen—" I was on the verge of suggesting that he might have it reproduced or multigraphed, as they called it, and distribute it about the department, but of course that was too preposterous a notion.

But again he considered gravely. He seemed determined to treat my views with formal respect. "Yes," he said. "It might account for the somewhat ostentatious style—it might indeed." Perhaps he had better see Willett—it would clear the air somewhat. The letter did, after all, offer an apology. I was the only one so far who had seen it, but very likely McLoon had intended it as a sort of public retraction.

He stood up decisively, shook hands again, thanked me for my patience and my unfailing something-or-other, smiled with unexpected warmth and softness—his mouth reflected an anxiety that the rest of him concealed. "I must be discreet, of course," he said. "The letter is by no means a published document. But your suggestion seems to me very helpful. I can recognize more clearly what I must do." Before he walked out he turned for a parting speech—he did it almost as though he were being directed in a dramatic scene. "Of course I reserve the right to speak my mind. McLoon is unworthy to occupy the position he does, and I shall say so to Willett and to the dean, possibly to the president. That much is my duty, as I am sure you will agree."

He went out.

It was my duty too, of course—or it would be if I agreed

with him. I certainly didn't like McLoon. But just a few days before one of my able students had been talking about him. "He's a great old bird," he said. "You know what they call him? Old Hundred Proof. There's nobody like him."

ss CHAPTER 14 ss

Harriet, of course, had no charity for attractive girls. If she even suspected my interest in one, she sharpened her weapons of mockery and ribaldry. All charming females, she knew, were by nature unscrupulous, and deadly. I was no better than a captive rabbit in their hands—I had no sense about women, I was a born victim. I was, of course, "sweet" —a word she often used against me; she meant I was innocent, naïve, foolish, inexperienced, in need of her constant protection. I had never really told her very much about my lost love Nora Martin, but somehow she knew, and she assumed that it was part of the expected folly of my behavior. And she had skill in ferreting out my interest in any female—at least in the earlier years. I used to ask students out to the house, the young writers and department assistants, and she could tell at a glance which girls were, as she candidly put it, dangerous. Not that *she* cared what went on—she was merely responsible for my general safety. It was her function to save me from public folly and disgrace.

178

Of late I have had less zeal for the student parties, perhaps to avoid the sardonic repercussions. The effort is always great—the arranging of time, giving out directions, checking on who can or cannot come, most of all the enlisting of Harriet as manager and hostess. Actually she enjoys parties of any kind, and she specially enjoys a group of students whom she can dominate and even, as she hopes, shock. "They equate all faculty wives with Sunday School teachers and librarians," she says. She adopts long cigarette holders and earrings for the occasion, and uses more profanity than she normally does. She used to have a kind of oriental costume which she called her harem suit, with folds of sheer red silk and black trimmings, and she posed as a lazy and somewhat sardonic sensualist. It was easier, of course, to impress young people twenty years ago, and I don't know that Harriet, with her in-grown habits, quite realizes how they are changing. She doesn't quite keep up with the plays they see and the books they read. Not that I "keep up" in any effective fashion, but I am more in touch with student habits—I read the sort of thing *they* write. Harriet poses very well, I must say. There's nothing inept about her performance, and I am sure students have enjoyed observing her and playing up to her. But I think they put a date to her. She may not emerge as a "librarian" but I have no doubt that they can label her in their own irreverent fashion. A suburban Auntie Mame, perhaps.

My first proposal of a party is usually met with disdain. Do we really have to go through that again? They seem so ridiculously young—every year they get younger. And their manners get worse.

Then the question of girls. Do I still have the Spanish countess? Harriet has never forgotten that the most glamorous and exquisite student I ever had, listed on my class roll as

Angela Montez, turned out to have a title and six names, three of them linked by a y. "Sandy absolutely grovelled," Harriet used to tell our friends. "He gave her straight A's. He arranged the most select parties . . . ." This was pleasant fooling, of course, and led to all sorts of merry jests, but actually my "Angela" has haunted me like a recurring romantic dream. She really existed, she sat in my class in a strange brightness of beauty and style, she wrote brilliant uninhibited papers in faultless English, she came to "confer" with me in my office, she came to one of our parties (only one), she behaved with the utmost charm and sweetness, and was altogether the most unbelievable heroine for grand romance I have ever encountered. Harriet's pretense that she was interested in me is simply part of her act. But I do dream of her; I see her adorning a tapestried castle. I hope some day to have a message, a sign.

It may sound as though I were more than ordinarily susceptible. I fell in love with Judith Samaris, for another example. And there was Margery, whom I haven't yet mentioned. But I think being "in love" in a pleasant, illusory way is a common condition with most people. It is the dream they live inside of. Not that I ignore the ecstasy and misery that often follow, or the intense secret life that exists behind the curtain of conventionality, even in the most inconspicuous of people—like me, for example. One source of Harriet's bitterness, I am afraid, is her failure to experience the actual intensities she thought she was entitled to. She held me responsible.

"To whom is your heart given this year?" she asked rhetorically. "What little Rachel or Sarah or Miriam?" She had an idea that more and more of my best students were Jewish. "Smart little cookies," she said. She professed to admire

Jewish girls because their heads were screwed on good and tight. "Watch out for them, though. They aren't about to be fooled. You may be, but not they."

I can't really say what it is in girls that wins me, but perhaps it is some kind of delicate candor. Harriet is more candid than almost anyone I know, and I can relish it in her; perhaps at the beginning, decades ago, there was some delicacy, or more grace in her, but now of course the bitterness dominates. I close my mind to it, or I take it as though it were directed to someone else. I am always magnetized by her, and it delights me to hear others speak of her with approval or respect—perhaps I am flattered to be part of her world and orbit. I recognize the strong character of it, and the energy and intensity she seems to create. But we never touch each other any more—no kissing or patting or lying together: not from any deliberate policy or decisive incident, but simply from gradual habit. Our bodies prefer to be separate, and she does most of her dressing and washing in privacy—more, at least, than wives normally do. At her age, she says, things like that are better done in secret. She fitted another bathroom in upstairs for her own use, and though we have two beds in what has always been our room she usually sleeps in the extra bedroom, where she can read at all hours of the night.

But the desire to touch and be touched is mysterious. I felt it strongly with Judith, in spite of my age—though I was at once so conscious of age that I suppressed it. Or tried to. I wasn't really put to any test. But with her, as with others, it is not simply the ideal body that attracts, the measurements and contours and texture of skin, though they obviously contribute; but more poignantly it seems to be something about the individuality. It is not her smile, but what particularly she smiles at—or what she sees, or hears, or is aware of. It is not really intelligence, at least in the conventional sense, but it is a hope and desire of the psyche, a thrilling conviction that the soul can at last find its mate. One knows the infinite delusions of such hopes, but they come with overwhelming force—and of course they come at quite unexpected and inappropriate times.

This Margery I named appeared first in one of my freshman classes back in the late thirties, a mouse of a girl who looked about fifteen, with no adornments whatever, no clothes or style or manner, hardly any articulate speech—if it ever came to be her turn to speak in class she was suffused in a total blush and her voice carried no further than the front row. But freshmen are expected to write about themselves, and it wasn't long before Margery was addressing me with a personal and almost secret intensity. And I found myself responding. We carried on a correspondence via her weekly themes, and a strong affinity built up. She came from a remote and mountainous part of Maine and her people were farmers and woodsmen, but her mother had been a schoolteacher, had even written a little book of old-fashioned poems, and Margery was living a private life of dreams. No creature could be more pure and sweet than she was. The possibilities in her world were all lovely, and she waited with infinite shyness and modesty for the revelations and fulfilments that she dreamed of.

It was she, actually, who made a point of capturing me, which is the sort of thing a modest girl can do better than anyone else. My intention is not to be cynical. The university oppressed and terrified her and she had to have a friend, as well as a guide and philosopher. She recognized me at once. A soul mate. She dreamed her dreams not so much to include me—she thought of me for quite a while as "old"—as to communicate them. There's no doubt that we "understood" each other, almost at sight, without need of explanations. She assumed that I would respond to all her little secrets, her favorite double-pawed cat, for example, or a nest of thrushes she saved from destruction, or the albino fawn she once saw in the woods, or the secret waterfall she visited alone, or the glade where fringed gentians blossomed in the fall. An old, lovely, poignant vision, almost, I suppose, a delusion: but I could share it—or at least I understood it. She read my novel about farm life and what seems quaint and far-off to other readers filled her with a sense of our communion. Even the sombre parts touched her. Not that she said anything for a long time, but she wrote with romantic passion. The farm life was going by, her grandparents were very old, her father drove twenty miles every day to work in a pulp mill, her brother was learning to fly airplanes. She half knew that her secret little yearnings were out of place, and every new week of her college life confirmed it. She was actually quite a sharp and competent scholar, and little by little she grew up, as we say—which means that she was able to examine and criticize her own illusions. But she held on to me for most of her four years there. She is married now—and I almost added "of course": a musician, or perhaps what is called a musicologist, a young man of intense self-importance who considers himself one with Bernstein and the late Monteux, with whom he studied, but is coordinator of music in a school district in central Maine. She sends Christmas messages.

The impulse to confess is very strong, of course. Margery had it in her young days, though her confessions were more sentimental and whimsical than in any way revelatory. Her only guilt was a sort of anger and impatience at her father for not perpetuating the life she dreamed about; he seemed to her, I gathered, rather brutal, though when I finally met him at her graduation he behaved with the patient modesty and pride appropriate to farmers and fathers. And of course as she matured and married and had children she put her childish ways behind her, as most normal people do. But those who are writers, who are designed to be professional poets or novelists, go on confessing all their lives. They turn themselves inside out in self-portraits and exploit the sins of their fathers, often very profitably. They dwell on the triumphs and tragedies of their private lives, along with friends, relatives, wives, and mistresses. There's a little burlesque by Jane Austen whose hero speaks out boldly. "No, never shall it be said that I obliged my father!" He was applauded for his noble manliness. This was long ago, in the eighteenth century.

I reflect on these things because this writing is more of a confessional than I wish it were. Aside from the strong lust of the ego which seems in itself ignoble, there are two excuses a rationalist can offer: one is that truth is great and must be served; the other is that a work of art justifies itself no matter what grief or shame or evil went into its making. The poet chronicling the brutal rape of his beloved, perhaps, is filled with his vision of the poem itself in all its brilliance and artfulness and "truth." I do have an interest in what we call truth, though it is a word without bounds or borders; our world is more and more dominated by professors, as I have already noted, and I conceive it a useful task to present them with as much candor and insight as I can achieve. The effort is worthy enough. But to record this minor love affair—at least in literal detail—seems unworthy: perhaps unworthy of the aim and end which I may have in mind. Names and circumstances are changed but my Margery is still up there in the north country, and some part of her is still the same girl. I am still fond of her, as the saying goes. If we met, anywhere, under any circumstances, we would see each other with a little smiling gleam of recognition. For the moment, at least, our psyches would meld. I would know this even if I were a very old man.

It was she who pursued me, as I have said, but she didn't quite know she was doing it, and being thoroughly female she did it artfully. When I teased her about it she at first denied it: it had never in her life occurred to her that she could do anything wrong, or that her natural and beautiful desires could lead her into a predicament that the world might call sinful. She was bewildered and hurt by any such suggestion. But then when we were in it, immersed and carried by the tide, our souls and to a certain extent our bodies merged and fulfilled, she was for a while wholly abandoned to delight. She grew more charming, and funny and whimsical and uninhibited; she laughed at everything and built up a whole code of jokes and humors. We walked along the river bank and shared lunch with the ducks, whom she named and pretended to be familiar with; and she eyed the babies and young mothers, and she made up stories about the loiterers and benchsitters, specially a bearded grandee in shabby clothes whom we always looked for—the Duke of Copley Plaza, she named him.

I felt as much like a father as a lover—and actually lover is not the right word. For a time we were soul mates, and I know no better phrase for it. We could walk on the esplanade in infinite happiness, borne along in a small shining cloud of our own. I could hear her talk in absolute confidence; she had a compulsive delight in telling me everything, even the traumatic secrets that girls keep to themselves, the first kiss from a lustful male, the near rape by a drunken woodsman, the sentimental dream about this or that boy. She spoke, as I remember her, observantly and well. She was really stimulated by her college experience, and perhaps by me, and seemed to be rediscovering her whole past in the light of her new attitudes. She told endless stories about Uncle Pete who lived up on the mountain and embodied all the legendary characteristics of the backwoodsman, an outlaw, poacher, deerslayer, as wily as a fox, as unscrupulous as a hawk, and infinitely charming to little girls. "He can tickle trout," she said, "He taught me how. Do you know I'm the only girl in the city of Boston who can tickle trout?"

She carried that country purity always with her, and I loved it. She had no apparent vanity of clothes or make-up. She wore generally a flannel skirt, and socks and flat shoes —she could walk endless distances. She liked being out in all weather, no matter how wet or cold—perhaps that was a vanity in her, and natural country toughness was her notion of true felicity. She like to display wet feet and wet hair. But there was something very magnetic about these habits—at least to me. I loved her homespun look, her bare legs still scratched from country brambles, her useful blunt fingers and short nails. I loved her soft untouched little-girl mouth and the smooth oval of her face—most of all I loved the shock of her light-brown hair combed carelessly back and sideways and secured by a head-band, usually a green one. Her eyes were brown with flecks of green and gold, and those were her usual colors. But there was something about the way her hair sprang back from her temples that gave me an acute anguish of love and pity. How infinitely sweet she was, how pure, how young, how hopeful. She lived in a careless eager rapture. She was a miracle of girlhood. She was as beautiful in her sex and youth as anything on earth. I could have wept for her—I suppose I did weep. There was nothing else to be done about it.

But conditions are relentless. We couldn't really be lovers—and even if we had been, what then? Middle-aged professor seduces trusting student. It happens, but awkwardly and often unhappily. There's no time or place. It is furtive. It feels guilty. It has no conclusion, unless it be disaster. But nonetheless, in spite of all this reasoning, I think Margery and I were good for each other.

It was she who pursued me—but I say it without the least implication of blame. She needed someone. She chose me. I used to find little signs on my office desk—at first anonymous, as though the good fairy had been in and out: a clipped photograph of her country perhaps, the remote Blue Mountains, or a funny cartoon, or a packet of elastic bands, or a chocolate bar. Later there were notes and little sketches, and a sort of code of references and jokes. In her outward habit she was as shy as one of her wild creatures in her mountains, but she had a natural inner force that was almost predatory. What she desired she would in the end achieve, but she would do it in a state of innocence and natural right; she would turn into an adult the way a kitten turns into a cat, secretly and inevitably. As Harriet has so often rightly observed, there is nothing more dangerous than a sweet girl.

Her most beguiling art was to take over my free time without making any demands on it. She remained always the very modest student, much too young and unimportant to interfere with professorial affairs. She quite genuinely believed that my knowledge was infinite in scope, my responsibilities were vast, my daily and hourly duties were mysteriously professional and complicated. She effaced herself. She slipped in and out of my office like a mouse. She assumed that she had no right of existence and was willing to disappear or to wait for indefinite time on a cold park bench—she expressed constant wonder and gratitude that I bothered with her or wasted my time with her. She alluded to my status, my rank, my degrees, my presumed reputation, with amused and whimsical humility—but never falsely, never with a poor-little-me pose. She was always—or nearly always—joyous in my company, and full of innocent pride and expectation. She came alive; her mind grew quicker, her eye more observant, her whole being brightened. She called me Dr. Sandy, with a flush of self-consciousness: most of the time she got along without calling me anything. In cold weather we sometimes went to movies, and in warm springs to baseball games. It seldom occurred to her that there could be anything indiscreet in all this, and if she occasionally raised the possibility she soon forgot about it. She was simply carried along on the wonderful tide of pleasure and adventure with a friend, father, and lover all at once in a new world of discovery.

As to what it meant to me, I find myself more evasive than I expected to be. How much wrong did I do? How foolish? How self-indulgent? Is it useful to go into all that—or is it really possible without rationalizing? My point that she grew and flourished in these years is right, I believe. Between us we lived with intense alertness and eagerness, and she expanded in awareness of life to such a degree that she took on distinction of character: she would be recognized in any company as a person to be admired. Whether this contributes to happiness is another question (Harriet says that only fools and children are concerned with happiness), but a fulfilment of the potentials of mind and heart is what we aim at in life, and by most criteria Margery has done well. If she suffered grief, and the agonies and angers of disillusion, she at least did so with what very simple people would recognize as dignity. I wish she had married a man with more natural humor.

But in view of my professorial responsibilities there's no doubt that I was too self-indulgent, or "weak." I allowed myself to be wholly beguiled by what some of my students would call a nymphet—not very aptly: she was in fact a woman, though extremely young. I found her irresistible—or almost so. The purity of her pleasures—her vision of wild animals, of brooks and trout, of rainy days and wind on water, of early mornings and new snow. And the shy and genuine humility that masked the strong character underneath, the steely persistence that carried her onward to an end she was hardly aware of.

It is too easy to talk of characteristics. What I loved immediately and palpably was the hair that grew back from her temples, and the oval of her face and the soft mouth with a twist of smile at the corners. And I suppose I was flattered by her need of me. She seemed to exist in a little Eden which I alone could share, and wherever we walked or sat or talked we were together in an absolute oneness of feeling and awareness, quite apart from surrounding life. She took in everything I said, however lightly or foolishly, and I was endlessly charmed by the play of thought and humor in her face. But as to what we said in all those communions, it wasn't worth recording. What do soul mates say to each other? They make pleasant and secret noises. They chuckle and touch and watch. They look out together through the same eyes at the preposterous comedy of life beyond the bounds of their own little garden. "There goes old By-and-Large," she would say, and I knew she meant our eminent geologist, Professor Doberman. "You mean Mud Puppy," I would answer at once. "By and large an extensive alluvial deposit," she would say in professorial tones, and then smile like a sprite.

We were almost too happy to speak at all.

This was all long ago. The age was by no means innocent, but, as Harriet always observes, I was—and perhaps inexcusably am. Margery and I drifted round together in parks and esplanades and corners of the library and lunch rooms and movie theatres. At first, for a long time, we were innocent companions—for a couple of years, in fact. We were of course observed. A city college is relentless in gossip but tolerant in attitude. Much goes on, intense and sometimes bizarre activities are noted, strange scandals that cause embarrassment to those in charge of what is called the public image, but the small devotions of young student to benevolent professor are to be expected. Jokes are furnished forth to deal with all aspects: my protégée, my disciple, my acolyte. I think the department thought better of me for having an attachment of that kind, though they could all have expatiated on the grave dangers involved. And I must say that Simon Partridge, who was our chairman at the time, would have been outraged at any suspicion of impropriety, but of course he never suspected anyone he approved of. So until toward the end we seemed to float along in a state of suspended innocence, unconcerned with sin or disaster.

Nor for a long time did Harriet take a hand in the comedy—which I suppose it actually was. She was in fact preoccupied with George Willett, and it is appropriately ironic, or even absurd, to imagine that while I was walking through park by-ways with my Margery she was entertaining the handsome Professor Willett.

But this is a fact that I know little about. I had a sort of notion, if that is an allowable term, but under the general circumstances of our living I put it aside, or postponed it, or turned it off. Perhaps my state was like one of those half-waking dreams where the sounds of real life come through, voices, lawnmowers, birds, cars in the street, but you cling almost passionately to the rich and strange visions in your dream. Any passage of early love is like that: you live most of the time in a state of hallucination, apart from what you ordinarily think of as reality. And when I had an anonymous note about Harriet and Willett I felt such disgust for the thing that I rejected it and was almost inclined to defend and justify them against any nasty allegations of that sort. Harriet did offend some of her neighbors, I knew, not by any special unpleasantness but merely by being her rather flagrant self, and some watchful housewife was getting back at her. She had a right to be what she was, in fact she couldn't help it, she was made that way, she . . . .

It sounds like abject rationalizing. I can only say that living with Harriet, in the same house with her, is not what I am best qualified to do. Yet I do it, and have for thirty years. And there are times when she seems to have special dazzle and even beauty, and I observe her with admiration. Perhaps I should say that there used to be such times.

But that anonymous note and all it hinted at was like one of the ugly sounds of reality breaking in and I rejected it as irrelevant and trivial. I preferred the illusions of my dream.

Yet the last spring grew more and more poignant. Margery's whole course of life had been virginal and she had no thought of changing it—at least no deliberate thought. She may have been simply afraid, as young girls are, but she was not blind or foolish. She was a farm girl, she knew more about animal affairs than I did; she had been to country schools and had coped with country boys and men. But her vision of herself was strict and controlled: she would be good, she would conscientiously mate and marry, she would be responsible. And of course she would be wonderfully maternal. In all the hours we were together, until the end, I don't think she ever thought of me as an actual mate. I was not part of her future—nor was she part of mine, though I always saw us together in lovely places, walking on mountains or resting in flowery meadows. It seemed to be understood that I was part of her growing up. "You're my major," she used to say. "That's what the kids keep telling me. 'Oh, you're majoring in Sanderling'."

But afterward, after it was all over, what then?

It came with a rush, the end. The spring blossoming and warmth, the culminating year, the duties and rituals, and the sense of finality. There were long silences in our last walks, and twined hands and arms, and furtive sideways glances. Love filled our minds, and if we had had a place to be secret in we would have gone there and made love: we were hardly aware of anything else. All sorts of stratagems occurred to me—and I'm sure to her too. It may be that we were balanced on the edge of a final resolution—or catastrophe. Or possibly triumph. I think about it a great deal still, twenty years later. But circumstances and old habits prevailed—just barely, just by the most trifling of chances. She did have a friend with an apartment—she told me this when it was too late: a girl with a nine to five-thirty job. But she couldn't bring herself to it—to be furtive, not considering herself, the insignificant one, but me, the respectable prof. But passion is of course no respecter of the decencies, and it was in the end only a matter of luck that we finished out what our observing world must have regarded as a minor academic comedy. If other chances had come along . . . .

After the last graduation exercises, with her parents there, whom I formally met, she had a remote frozen look. The smooth young face betrayed nothing, except eyes a little red from crying. No smile. Hardly a look. She had been working hard, they said; she needed to get home—she'd be fine once she got back to the farm—she could get to bed early—help with the planting—they hadn't got the corn in yet—

"Sandy," she said to me in the crush of people. "Sandy." She said it over and over. "I'll never be alive again."

๏ CHAPTER 15 ๏

Our daughter Joan was growing up in those days, and Harriet's purpose, as I said, was to train her in charm and brilliance. The true vocation of a girl, she felt, was to be an actress. All women had to act, one way or another, and there was nothing more dazzling and delightful than a really competent performer—not necessarily on a stage, or *the* stage, but in life, in drawing rooms, at parties. A well-equipped girl could sing, if called upon, or dance, or talk, or walk elegantly, or wear clothes, or be the life and spirit of any group. It is far from being a new or unusual theory, of course, but Harriet projected it more candidly than most mothers do. It isn't just a question of charm, or manner, it is an actual skill, it is being able to do it well. A girl who can stand up unaffectedly in a room full of people and sing a song is both giving pleasure and having pleasure: she is happy in her talent and success.

Harriet was much too shrewd to be an ordinary snob. She was merciless with any unworthy affectation, and she scorned the usual social and cultural vanities. But she did have a respect for the good performer in any field: she admired the elegant sophisticate who could get away with it, but woe to the poseur who couldn't. And she regarded herself as a special authority on the theatre and all its ways. One book case in our living room was devoted to her drama books. "My old illusions," she said, mocking herself.

But Joan—alas, Joan. She never came close to fitting any of the molds Harriet had in mind.

For one thing, she was too big. I don't know how it happened. Harriet is tall enough, and used to be graceful. I am about average. But by the time she was twelve Joan had that bulky cowlike shape and look that afflict some girls who are still designated as little. At dancing school she was supposed to perform with boys a head shorter and half her weight. It may have been one of her secret tragedies—though she never spoke of it; she has always been quiet about her troubles. Harriet in the end considered her insensitive ("cowlike"), but of course there's more to Joan than Harriet will ever admit. The two have never been able to touch in any of their natural orbits.

It has been assumed over the centuries that the sexes, to be accepted as normal, must exhibit certain traditional tastes. Girls must take to pink and ruffles. They must wear skirts, for reasons apparently of modesty, though no garment is less modest than a skirt. They must have bangles and ribbons. The compulsion for all this is somehow moral. If a man goes in for pink he is a menace to decent people. Anyway, Joan was always ludicrous in the customary feminine costumes; she wore them with the sad patience of a family sheep dog being decked out by whimsical children. Rebellion, at least in her child years, was not her style; she went along, she did what mother wanted; she accepted the rôles prescribed for her sex. But no little girl, or young girl, ever got dirtier than she did. It was as though she were compelled to roll in the earth—or burrow in caves, or crawl in attics, or as it sometimes seemed, slide down coal shutes. Harriet herself was not a fragile drawing room creature; she could dig and paint and paper walls—in those days, at least; but she did it with style, with appropriate slacks or smocks or figured kerchiefs for her hair. But Joan, no matter what feminine garments she started out with, usually came home looking like an old English chimney sweep—but never conscious of anything deplorable or even unusual about herself. The earth and all its dirt was her natural habitat. And of course the animals of earth. When she was six she began to keep snakes—she bought a snake from a little boy for ten cents and put it in a wooden box in our cellar with a window screen over it, but it disappeared almost at once and for months after we wondered if it still lived in some dark crevice in the cellar walls. From then on she acquired, at one time or another, toads, lizards, a gila monster, crawfish, guinea pigs, hamsters, rabbits, ducks, a monkey, mice, turtles, birds of all sorts, and of course dogs and cats. There was no way of stopping her—at least Harriet was unable to discourage or proscribe. She was amused up to a point, and made conversation-pieces out of her daughter's oddities: it was hilarious to find a snapping-turtle in the bathtub or lizards behind the kitchen stove—at least the anecdotes went well at parties. But the two characters and the two ways of life more and more opposed each other.

To say that Joan is not feminine is preposterous. She is a female of females, a sort of naturalistic mother; early cultures would probably adopt her as their Venus symbol. But she is obviously nothing like the representative dream-women that figure in our romantic visions. She is built solidly, with a thick waist, stout legs, big breasts; she could be fat if she allowed it, but she works like a man and has the strength of a man. She is not muscular in any outward way—in fact she has what I think is a lot of feminine beauty: her skin is velvet and flushed with good health, her eyes are full of warm brown lights and kindliness, her mouth is soft and big, her teeth strong and even and very white. Her brown hair is clipped as short as a man's and is seldom combed. She wears the basic practical things, and is indifferent to styles.

But she is probably too indifferent, or too preoccupied with her little world. She is really kinder to animals than she is to her fellow men—or at least she is more aware of them. She is practical. She does all that is needed. She treats her husband like a working associate and takes care of him and everything else—house, children, animals, farm—such as it is. There's something primordial about her; she is the basic woman of all human history, the one who does the work, bears the children, heals the sick, manages unceasingly from day to day forever. To ask if she is happy would be impertinent, or if she "loves" her husband or family, or if she is an adequate wife according to women's magazine standards. She doesn't bother with such considerations. She works—and manages and feeds and nourishes and fosters life of all kinds: she is pleased by achieving a good dinner for a company, or by saving a cow's life, or delivering a calf that needs expert help.

But I know what Harriet means when she says the girl has no feelings. She makes no distinction between taking care of her own children and a litter of retriever puppies—or welcoming her father, say, and greeting a neighbor dropping in to borrow a hedge clipper. At least that is the outward impression one gets from her. We think of most people, or certainly the sensitive and interesting ones, as having an inner life, or as carrying on a sort of running commentary on how things are going in their affairs, but Joan seems to take everything as it comes, major or minor, outer or inner. She spends her whole energy and time in doing things.

Yet I too easily forget. She must have set herself early to resist Harriet, and those stoical habits were built up like muscles. I find myself blaming Harriet: it is her "fault" that Joan is what she is; and then I say, as fathers do, that it is my "fault." Parents always say these things, no matter what the state of their children is. But along in Joan's teen years, Harriet did attack her relentlessly, day after day, almost minute by minute. Nothing passed unobserved, and Harriet's sardonic comments on clothes, manners, behavior, taste, every twist and turn of Joan's daily life, grew more and more cruel. "Honestly, child, you look more like Tugboat Annie than Annie herself does. I'll bet you've been tucking away french fries by the carton—" Joan did eat too much, of course, and the french fries could be bought at a lunch wagon near her school—a box full for twenty cents. Joan had a fine complexion no matter what she ate, but she was bulky—even when she played girls' hockey, which she was good at. Harriet kept up the pressure—for what she considered appropriate experience in music, theatre, social affairs (though of course she assumed that the debutante racket, as she called it, was wholly preposterous). But Joan had to be inspected, prodded, pulled and pushed, and inevitably disapproved of. "What in God's name am I going to *do* with you?"

What can a father and husband do? Obviously great strength and courage are needed in these crises, and I had neither. "She can't help being what she is," I mumbled. Let her alone, let her be—I couldn't say it. Not effectively, anyway. Harriet was possessed. "Of course she can help it! Damn it all, we'd be savages if we were let be. Civilization has to be *learned*." But her notion of civilization derived from her own temperament. If Joan had not been her daughter and the symbol, at first, of her hopes, she could have accepted her and taken note of the virtues she had. And actually Joan always stood high in the opinion of others—teachers and neighbors and friends, who considered her more dependable and competent than other girls, and somehow entertaining in her earthy habits. But the tensions at home increased to an unbearable degree, and Harriet's frustrations enveloped us all. She naturally held me to blame for a good deal of the trouble, since Joan obviously inherited her habits from the Sanderlings (some of whom had once been farmers), and in time I suffered ulcer pains and went on a diet. "If you'd just get mad and have a good *rampage*, you'd be better off," Harriet used to say. "You're all compressed inside that old-fashioned shell of yours—no wonder you nearly explode. Look at me—I behave like a star-spangled bitch—I'm not about to have ulcers." She only said that, of course, in a state of reckless good humor. Actually those years of Joan's adolescence seemed to drain what was left of her youth and bring on the witchlike look of bitterness and contempt that she will carry into old age. It wasn't only Joan and her problem that caused it, of course, but for a time that was the main issue.

So instead of going to one of the suitable liberal colleges for girls which Harriet selected, Joan got herself accepted at the state university, where she could study "animal husbandry," as it was still called (I can hear Harriet's voice as she dwelt on the ironies of that phrase), and in six months, along in early spring, she married Leroy Kramer. Joan does what she does with slow and even resolution, like a natural force. It isn't evident that she is the kind who would obviously attract a lover or husband, yet her marriage at her age of nineteen did seem inevitable, and so did the five children who followed at less than two-year intervals. They live near Port Jervis, on the edge of a semi-wild region of woods and hills, and Leroy teaches mathematics and coaches athletic teams. Their ambition is to stay there the rest of their lives.

She wanted at first to be a professional doctor of animals, and did some of the preliminary studying, but marriage and children interfered, and she settled down to be content on some country acres where she could keep any number of animals and make a small business of raising chinchillas—not ever very profitable, I believe. She is known for miles around as an expert on the cure and care of all living creatures.

What really troubles Harriet is the sense of her failure. She intended to prevail, and she didn't. It came to be a major issue, perhaps the greatest of her life, and she fought it out with every intention of winning. She applied her will and wits to the utmost. I told her once that she was acting like King Canute trying to command the sea, and for a long time she resented it; she considered Canute a dolt, of course, but she was never willing to concede her own defeat, and the notion that she herself was being foolish was not admissible. "I certainly had the right to assume that my daughter was capable of learning the rudiments of civilized living. She could be a changeling, of course. I can't think of any other explanation for her."

It seems harsh, but just lately she can speak of Joan and her family with a somewhat softer humor. There are four boys and a girl growing up in what she considers primitive ignorance, and when I go off to visit them in summer she hopes I can interest them in something other than animal reproduction. As for Leroy, she has never yet met him, but she pronounces his name only in accents of amused scorn. Lee-roy, "your son-in-law." She thinks she knows all about him; she assumes he is a big lummox with no brains. His great achievement in life was to play on his university foot-ball-team—and to be considered a potential professional. Harriet is probably right about him, given her conception of what a lummox is, but no one in the world is more good-natured than Leroy Kramer.

What I am mainly getting at is that when I go to visit them, in late July after my summer teaching, I pass from one element to another. It is a long trip, mostly on a bus. I leave New England behind and enter the foreign countryside of the Delaware valley where the look of the houses and woods and fields is somehow different, and Dutch-sounding names like Cuddeback and Terwilliger appear on mail boxes. Joan lives off in the hill country in a cross-road village called Markham Corners, where pioneer farms once prospered but are now reverting to trees and brush: there is a sad little white Lutheran church, a store with gas pump, a few non-descript houses close up to the road. Hers is like that too, north of the corners, with nothing in sight beyond it and fields stretching up to a wooded mountainous ridge in the northeast. The house is tall and narrow and shabby-white, with a rather fancy front porch bordering the very edge of the road: at first glance you think it is a big house, with decorative trimmings here and there, but the actual structure is so meagre and unimaginative that its effect is one of pathos. The old phrase for it might be shabby-genteel, in the forlorn and pretentious manner of the last century, but it hardly comes up to that level. Yet it stands, keeps out rain and cold, provides rooms for a family of seven, allows for the essentials of indoor living. Joan has no vision of ideal felicity—and certainly Roy doesn't. What they want are things that work, indoors and out, and their equipment is all practical. What they most admire is the complex of barns, sheds, pens, corrals, garden plots, and land running on indefinitely into fields and woods.

At first when I come I feel so alien as to be embarrassed about it, like the tenderfoot or "dude" of old pioneer romances. The place inside and out is loud with its own life, the boys shouting and charging about, Roy making himself heard no matter what else is going on, dogs barking—all in the best of humor. Joan seems to have no nerves, and no concern about details. Things happen, crashes, spills, wounds—she is not visibly disturbed. Meals come when they come, without ceremony, with vast consumption. Talk is carried on by whoever can shout loudest—and though Joan herself has never been much of a talker she can shout when she has to. Her instinct for controlling creatures of all sorts is quite wonderful: she never checks her boys, or nags at them, or seems to command them, and they do what they please with complete animal vigor, but they are full of responsibility and concern for the general welfare. It is a kind of miracle, and I give Joan credit for achieving it, but I'm sure she has no conscious plan or even awareness that she is doing it. Perhaps the secret of it is the basic good health they seem to have, and a respect for needs of all living things.

I have a pleasant sense of irresponsible adventure when I go there, not unlike my feelings when I visited the old farm as a boy. Another world and life, more primitive and perhaps more real. Each time I come I have to be initiated. I visit the mysteries of the chinchilla cages and am told about their births and deaths and their strange private habits and their nasty dispositions. My grand-daughter leads me to admire the golden calf she is raising to show at the country fair in October—she will win a ribbon, she hopes: in fact, she seems to be quite sure of it. (Her name is Maribel, which Harriet considers preposterous, of course; it goes with Lee-roy and Chesley, who is the youngest boy—and she can't pronounce them without an accent of mockery.) Another of the boys, Little John, spends his time training a bird dog, and takes me with him into the back country to show how it is done—he instructs and lectures me, in fact, and takes it for granted that I know nothing about anything.

But that old farm of my grandfather's was a whole culture, a microcosm of a time. It stood for a world, with manners, morals, talents, aims, going on from generation to generation: men and women were born and grew up in it, were encompassed by it, given essential purpose by it, challenged and tested by it, recognized and honored in their earthly successes. But here at Markham Corners the little world they live in is only a minor enclave, a sport, an effort to escape.

Or so I said to Joan. "You're all happy here," I said.

"I guess so," she answered. She was always reluctant to come to conclusions.

"Can you live all your lives this way?"

"What do you mean?"

I am not good at giving advice on how to live. Willett can do it—I hear him saying, "Well, what you ought to do is this . . ." The words echo from his office when the door is open. That's the way chairmen talk. "My advice to you is to apply at Michigan and . . . ."

But I raised the question, at least. What will the young ones *do*—in the long run, that is. They can't devote themselves to raising calves and bird dogs—or can they?

Joan hardly admitted the question. "I'm not worried," she said. She smiled serenely. "They can if they want."

"Well," I said, "the world—" What I meant was plain enough, but it seemed futile to try to say it literally. Joan lived apart from these considerations—so did Roy, who was even less concerned with the "world" than Joan herself.

"I guess you think we are little frogs in a little puddle," she said.

It was about it. "A very nice puddle," I added.

She roused up. I could see her begin to think. "What are you recommending for us?"

I had in mind, of course, the long business of schooling, such as I was used to: four years of college, up to four years more of graduate school. It was a formidable prospect for a family of five children. So far they seemed to live in happy disregard of such demands: it would surprise me, in fact, if the children ever get themselves through high school—though with their father as coach of football they might have some incentive. But they lived with no signs of intellectual tastes— no books, no good music, no awareness that the world at large is full of very complicated ideas.

"I don't know," Joan said. "What do you think it is really all about? What are they doing out there—in New York, or Boston, or Newton? Is that where people are happy? Are you, for instance? I know Mother isn't. That isn't fair, I guess—to mention her; but I mean people out *there*, in cities . . . ." She waved a hand at them. "What are they living for?"

It was remarkable that she would say as much as that.

She looked rather embarrassed, as though a discussion of life's purposes were not quite decent. Her naturally pink face was a little pinker than usual. I think actually she assumed that because I was an elderly professor with mysterious resources of knowledge and wisdom she had no business arguing with me at all.

"I'm afraid my notion of life is pretty simple," she said.

But actually, I had no wiser answers—none at least that I could insist on. People do live to be happy, they pursue it as a goal, as we have formally declared, but deliberate pursuit usually ends in failure. I said that, and quoted Harriet, who has always been cynical about the possibility of happiness. But then I drew back, I reconsidered, as I too foolishly do. Some ways of life are pleasanter than others, some are free and beautiful and some are not.

Perhaps it comes down to the question of fulfilment, I said. Joan herself seemed to be fulfilled. She used all her faculties. She had no large visions, but she provided the sort of immediate life and liberty that satisfied her. So also, I thought, did Roy, the good-natured lummox, though I didn't put it that way. But what of the growing girl and the boys? Suppose they were potential doctors or lawyers or scientists or professors.

Our talk was at night after all the others had gone to bed. We were sitting at the dining room table, which seemed to be the nerve-center of the house—where games were played and handiwork done and conversations carried on at all hours.

"But here we are," Joan said. "What can we do about it?"

"Perhaps you could let one of them come and live with us—I mean, of course, if he wanted to. We could help with the college problem—"

"Mother wouldn't stand for it," she said.

I replied that her mother was a complicated person whom she didn't really appreciate. If she thought she was rescuing a child from a life of rural ignorance, she would certainly do it. Especially her own grandchild. "She has some fine ideals, you know."

I could see Joan slowly withdraw into herself. "I probably don't appreciate her," she said. "But really, she—" For a moment she seemed too frustrated to speak. Then she waved a hand. "She's so *unhappy*." Her face had grown pinker again. She spoke in a low voice. "She almost destroyed me, you know. She almost killed me."

She had never put it so literally before. I couldn't say anything intelligible. "Surely—" I mumbled, but got nowhere.

"Don't you think she'd begin all over again if she had Maribel, say, or Little John?"

Actually I didn't think so, but it was all so conjectural. I sat there for a while in silence.

"It seems miles and miles away," she said. "It seems like another world."

That's it. Out there at Markham Corners, far, far away, is a little enclave of basic existence, carried on like a relic of primitive ritual. Earth is plowed and planted, a cow is milked, hens lay eggs, food and shelter are provided—all quite regardless of science and the arts, and wars and rumors of wars.

Here in greater Boston, as it is called, I live in a universe of technology.

Professors come to think there is nothing real but that. They live and die among their theories and skills, they write for each other and about each other. Their horizons are bounded by learned journals and critical journals. They take

theoretical stands on all political and social affairs, support-
ing or opposing their intellectual colleagues. They are surrounded by the numberless students who are competing and
competing to follow in their steps.

⋐§   CHAPTER 16   §⋑

Ordinarily I saw very little of Mark Jaeger, our Victorian authority. It seemed to be assumed that he and his wife didn't "go about," but I'm afraid the fact is that they simply were not invited: at least they were not invited among the ones we usually met at dinners. They sometimes appeared at the occasional large cocktail party, where they seemed to stand somewhat apart from the rest of the company—specially Mrs. Jaeger, who always had an immovable, rocklike look to her. She was actually taller and bigger than her husband, and most of us were intimidated by her—mainly because she said so little and looked so fierce. She was also, as I have said, so much older that the effect was a little embarrassing, and newcomers were very apt to assume she was his mother—a circumstance that naturally led to jests and ironies. She was said to be learned, and had published articles (in German) on Sumerian pottery; she spoke perfectly grammatical English but pronounced all the *th*'s like *z*'s and had trouble with *w*'s. It was very difficult to carry on small talk with her.

"Ah, Mrs. Jaeger," Willett might say with his best smile. "How do you do? So nice you could come."

"Professor Villett, is it not? Zank you, I am in excellent health. And you—you are quite vell, I hope?"

None of us ever got much beyond that point with her, at least at cocktail parties. Her face had set itself in a mold which made it difficult for her to smile, but the sculptured lines of it were deep-cut and splendid. With her helmet of steel-gray hair she looked medieval, and except for her clothes not in any essential way feminine. She certainly couldn't unbend and be loquacious among us, but I have heard her chatting in her native language with the utmost intensity and solemnity of expression, and I can't help feeling that she has decided that Americans and the American language are not worth serious consideration. I'm probably being unfair. She and her husband communicated in English in public, at least. But we all tended to be sorry for him.

If we could have liked him more, we'd be sorrier. But he made it almost impossible. His constant assumption was that everything we did was shoddy. Our standards were low. Our students were second-rate. Our own scholarship was deplorable. Our publishing record was embarrassing. At any mention of our plans or hopes, he sniffed—he could sniff more eloquently than anyone I know. "Perfectly futile, really—" I can hear the words wrapped round a quiet sneer. Yet if he wanted to he could speak with a good deal of charm—he prided himself on his manners and his fastidiousness and his recognition of all that is high and austere and even elegant.

I mention elegance because he did have some sort of vision of it, even to the extent of being considered effeminate. There were inevitable whispers about sexual deviations, but I know nothing about it—except that his marriage relationship hardly seemed normal. I suppose his scholarly devotion to Victorian pornography was excessive also. You could tell by looking at him that he was a special sort of person, at least in university circles: he was always perfectly dressed, with matching details and very shining leather-soled shoes. He wore elegant hat, coat, and scarf. He carried a tightly rolled umbrella. Most of us, of course, take to loose tweed jackets and colored shirts and no hats, but not Jaeger. He went about with a vision of Deportment in his mind, like Mr. Turveydrop in *Bleak House*, though he was far from being a semi-idiot. He spent much time in London, presumably carrying on his bibliographical studies of Dickens and other Victorians, and his appearance somehow reflected that background.

It was generally noted that when he went to London his wife went elsewhere, with professional purpose—to Germany or some remote diggings in the East. She had a son in East Germany too, and other links with a past life, but we were told almost nothing about all that. They seemed to have no family connections or dependents here.

When Jaeger first came as an instructor some twenty years ago he had already developed his significant sniff, and an effective lift and twist of his chin that seemed to make further discussion useless. He looked old then, for a man not yet thirty; in time he looked young for a man not yet fifty. He never, in fact, seemed to change. He had the tight death's-head look that young scholars develop, with shiny, semi-bald skull, high forehead with bumps on it, hollow cheeks, strong chin, and a thin fastidious mouth marked with bitterness. "It's all perfectly futile"—that's what he seemed to be saying, or sniffing, with the slight upward twist.

If you asked him about his origins he said at once that his

people lived in Milwaukee (he put it in the past tense). He said his father had been a brewer. He said it quite sharply and candidly, as though it had a humorous point to it. His accent was noticeably Oxford, where he studied once, with overtones of a special elegance that probably derived from Harvard, where he got his degrees. You can see that he presented a very distinguished and formidable aspect.

I remember how enthusiastic both Partridge and Willett were when he came. We all admired his credentials. Brilliant record, Partridge said; strongest recommendations—undoubtedly a sound man. Fine scholarly promise, Willett said. We need a good research man, specially in bibliography. I might add that every new man comes in with infinite promise; we regard him always with a thrill of hope and a jealous fear that he will expose our failures. And perhaps as far as I am concerned that's what Jaeger did, because one of his first acts was to attack and dismember a doctoral dissertation I was supposed to be responsible for. It dealt with an obscure novelist of the early eighteenth century named Eliza Heywood, whom no one ordinarily knows anything about. Fulmar and I had "accepted" it, and the various routines were going along quietly, when Jaeger happened to glance at it. In two minutes he was fuming with disapproval. The bibliography was inadequate—it didn't mention Garlitz's definitive study of the early women writers of England; in fact, he went on, none of the important German scholarship was cited, and he presumed the man was simply incompetent to deal with it—like most of our so-called doctoral scholars, he added. His sniff and tilt of chin were terribly in evidence—and his fastidious accent. He went on to note that the bibliographical format of the thesis was quite impossible—there was improper word order in the footnotes, and irregular punctuation. It was lucky for me that Fulmar happened to be on hand to speak up for it, as he did with a great deal of nervous indignation. But the whole matter blew up into a departmental hassle, with a meeting of the Graduate Committee and the application of some anxious diplomacy. I have felt ever since that Jaeger was probably right, but the fellow got his degree and has lately written the best biography we have of Fanny Burney, so I try to reassure myself about him.

And then Jaeger took over one of the courses I taught, the Victorian Novel—which in those disorganized times (it was right after a major war) was one of the large catch-all courses that almost anyone could elect. He was furious at the whole set-up. He had eighty students in it, three-fourths of whom were incompetent, and one-third of those illiterate. There were students from business, nursing, education, and something called public relations—he pronounced these words in a crescendo of distaste. He said it was all perfectly preposterous—in fact, futile. The course was a travesty.

I had once again the miserable feeling that he was probably right, and realized that I had been running the whole thing like a sort of cultural circus, with readings from Dickens's funniest passages. Jaeger succeeded in changing all that, and in several years reduced his enrollment to an austere thirty or less, with stern devotion to the obligations of scholarship. He also encouraged some of his graduate students to go in for "advanced research," but one of our main topics of gossip in the department was to wonder what new secrets he and his disciples were discovering among the private lives of respectable Victorians.

So far as any of us knew, he published virtually nothing—not even any parts of the thesis that was said to be so brilliant. He gave no papers at "meetings," though I think he was faithful in attending the important ones. But all this is part of his past, and I write about him almost as though he had led two lives. When they first came we made social overtures, met them at the usual receptions, and invited them to dinner—once. Harriet said she couldn't stand either of them; she needled them, enough to make me quite uncomfortable, but they apparently didn't notice it. Mrs. Jaeger seemed unaware of irony, specially in an American idiom. Jaeger had a somewhat insulated air, as though he lived at a slight remove from the rest of us, with a set of values we obviously failed to perceive, but he could talk readily—specially about the amenities of life in London as contrasted with the vulgarities of America. It occurs to me as I think back that he spoke always in terms of what were really cultural clichés. His theme was dear old London. Or charming old Oxford. Or the pleasures of working in the Bodleian—or the British Museum where you saw such wonderful characters, and of course such distinguished ones too. He alluded at times to Sir Harold or Lord David. He assumed we all admired his views. He took it for granted that we also were oppressed by the low estate of our culture and surroundings. "You find everything here pretty futile, no doubt," Harriet said in a dangerous voice, but he seemed impervious to her irony. The evening passed without the open hostilities I feared. "There's something about that man," she said afterward. "It's all a cover, a grand impersonation. What do you think is really underneath? Is she his keeper, his governess?"

But after that we saw little of them—in a social way. There were occasional big gatherings to which they dutifully came; she seemed to make a special point of being seen, and sometimes actually appeared at such affairs when he didn't. "Professor Jaeger regrets zat he cannot be here on ziss occasion." She always made the same speech, repeated like a recording. I saw him, of course, in our departmental business, and met him here and there in the halls. A year ago he went away on a year's sabbatical.

Last fall he returned and took over his courses again, but I didn't see him for several weeks—nor, I gathered, did anyone else. It was known that he was back, and presumably carrying on, and I supposed Willett was in touch with him. But in a department like ours there is no formal checking-up on what goes on, at least on the upper levels. Medrick is supposed to keep a responsible eye on the new instructors and teaching fellows, as they are called—and he does so very benevolently; but a man "on tenure," like Jaeger, may remain unseen indefinitely. He makes his own plans and consults his own conscience. Sometimes strange rumors turn up—and Professor So-and-so is said to have spent the month of March in Antigua, while his students were "doing independent research." I remember how furious Partridge was when old Theophilus Beaker went off to England in the middle of a semester by steamer, because he said he had to verify a line in Milton—a phrase, by the way, which has become a minor refrain with us ever since. It is our academic equivalent of seeing a man about a dog. For the most part, though, we insist on the privilege of minding our own business. Jaeger was presumed to be doing his job, and that was that.

But rumors began to build up. Students mentioned that Professor Jaeger must be unwell. His lectures, one said, were almost inaudible. One day he simply walked out in the middle of the hour, without a word or gesture. Sometimes he didn't appear at all. He could be very touchy and "difficult": he seemed to expect them to remember all sorts of bibliographical stuff, but was furious if anyone asked questions. I even spoke to Willett about him, and wondered if anything was wrong—I mentioned the rumors I had been hearing. But he knew nothing about it. "Well, you know how Jaeger is—he can be damned difficult. He's pretty tense this fall, I realize—I guess he works too hard, or he thinks he does, which amounts to the same thing. He takes himself pretty seriously."

I met him one day between classes in a faculty room: there were two or three others coming and going, and he was standing at a window with his back to us. It was one of the lovely Indian summer days, and I remarked on it. I thought of saying something about "hushed October," which is a phrase from a Frost poem, but restrained myself: it is always embarrassing to hear anyone quote verse, at least with senti-mental intent. "Beautiful day," I said, though I realized at once that that didn't sound right either. But when he turned I saw that he hadn't heard the words. He stared at me with opaque eyes, magnified by thick-lensed spectacles. His face and skull had always had a death's-head look to it, with the whiteness, the hollow cheeks, the high boney forehead, but now suddenly I was shocked by a sight of death itself. His mouth was drawn back, his eyes seemed to be glazed over, his skin was like paste.

"You don't look well," I said.

"Oh, Sandy," he said with a sudden effort. "Is that you? How have you been?" The echo of polite elegance was in his tones, but remotely.

"Are you all right, Mark? You—you've certainly been los-ing weight, haven't you?" It almost surprised me that he rec-ognized me. There was no movement in his eyes. "Are you ill?" I said.

A buzzer sounded, and I gathered myself to head for class.

I spoke again, reminded him of the time, left him staring at the window glass.

For a few days the vision of his face stayed in my mind like an apparition. I spoke of it to others, but no one had really seen him. He was not in his office. Not at faculty meetings. A heavy responsibility began to weigh on me. I thought of making an excuse to call him or visit his apartment or even to consult with his wife, but I hardly knew what good I could do. But one afternoon I saw him from my window, a neat smallish figure with hat and Burberry topcoat and rolled umbrella and briefcase, standing motionless on a path along the river bank. Something impelled me to run out to intercept him, though I certainly had no conscious plan in mind. I did feel a small inner panic; not so much because of any belief in Jaeger's troubles as because of my own rash act of breaking in upon his privacy. I had certainly never been close to him.

"Is that you, Mark? You don't usually come this way. Are you heading down town?"

In the days of his normal vigor his mouth had expressed a kind of final certainty. It closed over its pronouncements as though it were seated and sealed, like a carefully made beak. Now as he looked at me his mouth remained open and a little askew. The knot of his tie had slipped just enough to reveal the button.

"Something is bothering you," I blurted out. "Is there anything I can do?"

"No, oh no—" He said it with a far-off sound. Then his old manner asserted itself. "Thank you—it is good of you to be concerned. There is really nothing—nothing anyone can do." But his eyes hardly seemed to focus on me. "It is all quite —quite—" I thought he was going to say "futile"; there was an echo of a sneer.

Is there anything I can do: everybody says it in times of misery and death. It seemed clear to me that there was nothing I could "do," but I persisted. Perhaps I could take a class or two for him. Perhaps a few days' rest . . . .

I mentioned health again. A doctor, a hospital examination—they are wonderfully thorough, I said.

We strolled along. He was unaware of what he did. We sat on a bench, facing the water. It was a hazy still day, with smoke in the air and a pale sun. My efforts to talk might have seemed embarrassing but I felt that it didn't really matter what I said. I could as well have discussed football.

"You know, Sanderling," he said with sudden strength, almost as though he were about to lecture, "I recognize that I am an imposter. I state it as a fact in evidence—"

I interrupted. We are all imposters, I said. We authorities and professional wise men—

But he talked. I don't know that he really was aware of me sitting beside him, but he talked.

Eighteen years out of graduate school and he hadn't yet published. All his work, he now realized, was worthless. All his pretensions to serious scholarship. All his life's hopes and expectations . . . .

"Oh, come," I said. "Look at the rest of us. We're all in the same boat, you know."

A twitch of smile indicated a vast superiority to any comparisons I could offer. But it was simply a habitual sneer going through its little muscular sequence, with twist of chin and precise closing of lips. He was still unable to take note of me as an individual.

I went on with some soothing and sensible remarks about scholars and teachers. Writing learned articles is not neces-

sarily proof of wisdom. Many fine teachers publish nothing—look at Willett, for one, or Medrick. My argument, I
realized, was so familiar as to be a sequence of clichés, but I
felt impelled to put it as strongly as I could. I knew, though,
that as far as Jaeger was concerned it was actually irrelevant.
He had staked his professional life on the learned-article
approach; he had castigated us for years on our failure to do
our scholarly duty.

"What's gone wrong?" I said. "You must have had a shock
of some sort." I wondered, of course, if it had to do with his
wife, whom I hadn't seen since before the sabbatical year.
Had she been attacking him, had she left him? Or was it
something about the sabbatical? Had something happened in
England? "Is—er—Mrs. Jaeger over here," I ventured, "or
has she gone back to Anatolia?" I couldn't bring myself to
refer to her as Hilda, though it was considered proper in the
department to use first names.

But I was not getting through to him.

His major effort, he said, had been an exhaustive study of
Edwin Drood. He had examined all of Dickens and all of
Collins, all the notes, the title pages, the illustrations and
decorations, the relevant letters and rumors and biographical
implications. We had known this, of course; his students
were everlastingly writing papers on the mysteries of *Edwin
Drood*, and theories as to what Dickens would have done
with it if he had lived. "Trying to imitate Dickens is the
height of folly, of course," he said. "But I did so—I made a
study of his vocabulary and sentence structures, his habits of
caricature and sentimentality and vulgarity, his unconscious
symbolism—I even resorted to computers."

I caught some of his despair as I listened. But I spoke up
with an attempt at good cheer. "Surely there is usefulness in

this," I said. "Why take it so hard?"

"Tell me, Sandy," he said, rousing up, "do you consider me a pedantic ass?" He reached and snapped open his briefcase. "You have seen this, no doubt. I assume it has circulated widely—things like this always do. It is kind of you to make no mention of it, of course—" He held and studied a rather dog-eared manuscript, then thrust it at me. "It's rather good, you know. Almost too good for an undergraduate. It could be the work of one of our precocious colleagues, wouldn't you say?"

Three or four pages of typed verse entitled "The New Dunciad" and addressed with elaborate compliments to Professor Mark Aaron Jaeger. I hadn't seen it, but I could tell at once that it was a carefully worked-out satiric attack—actually a sort of poison-pen letter in heroic couplets. Even a quick glance gave me lines I haven't forgotten:

> He comes with well-bred sneer and well-stuff'd shirt
> To rub our noses in Victorian dirt.

"I don't let it bother me too much," he said, with a touch of agony. "After all, I am accustomed to the slings and arrows. But anonymous attacks are always indecent. One begins to have inevitable suspicions." He glanced at me almost as though he at last realized that I was there. "I do very much appreciate your solicitude, Sandy. You are a good colleague. You—you mean to be kind, I am sure. I can't say that about many in our department, as you must agree. Human nature at its worst, malice, envy, vanity—we are well surrounded by those." He seized the typed pages and shook them in emphasis.

"Surely," I said with a sense of my helplessness, "you malign our colleagues."

"Who knows? There are a number I can easily suspect."

"It's simply one of those exercises in imitating Pope," I said. "They do it every year in Fulmar's course—you remember the time Stevenson ran for president, one of them wrote an 'Adlaiad.' It's just a stunt—"

But of course he wasn't listening. I tried to point out that some students took pleasure in viciousness—it was almost a fad. Sadism, I understood, was in.

"You are too childish, Sandy," he said, irrelevantly I thought. "You don't really know what's going on; you live in a nice little country world . . . ."

Is that how they see me? Perhaps it is. There was no point in my arguing, anyway. He was concerned with other things.

"You may," he said with forced irony, "be amused at some of these items too." He brought out a thick manilla envelope. "Rejections—all very polite. Letters from distinguished editors—as well as undistinguished underlings. They unanimously regret. They find my work—" He couldn't bring himself to say it. He thrust a letter at me. "Note this one, for instance." It had a London heading, and was a formal rejection of a manuscript, couched in respectful terms: but it included a copy of a reader's report, with the candid and devastating phrases of direct judgment. Trivial. Pedantic. Blind to the nature of the subject it dealt with, which of course was the genius of Charles Dickens.

I confess I had a mean satisfaction at reading this, and I'm ashamed. Here was a man in the full agony of despair, and I was taking some credit to myself for trying to come to his rescue, for "doing something" for him. But I had spent years disliking him and wondering if he were some sort of charlatan after all. I had never heard him express a useful or interesting idea; I remembered the clichés and platitudes he had offered from time to time. I also remembered the officious attacks on our various operations, specially of course on my own. Now at last a kind of ultimate judgment had been rendered.

"This also," I said, "is a universal experience for writers. There's a kind of distinction in having an ample folder of rejections." Is it hypocritical to say a thing like that? I assumed that nothing I could say would have much effect.

"I made a last major effort in England. I worked very hard—" His face had gone slack again as though it had begun to melt. The mouth stayed open. "This was my final hope."

"You overdid," I said. "You are obviously exhausted . . . ." By now I was simply making soothing noises.

"And Hilda, of course—" He laughed with an almost childish sound.

I had wondered about her all along. "What about—Hilda? Isn't she—?" I couldn't think how to say it.

But he seemed to recede into misery. He sat apart from me, staring at nothing. I had a strong conviction that Hilda was really at the bottom of his trouble, and it occurred to me (unworthily, I suppose) that if she had really left him he ought to be feeling free and relieved. But I assumed she had had some strong maternal hold on him. It is probably evident by now that I don't really understand such a character as Jaeger's.

I spoke somewhat irrelevantly. "Do you mean you have been *imitating* Dickens?" I pitched my voice rather sharply in the hope of distracting him. "You've been writing *Edwin Drood* as you think he would have written it if he had lived?"

My notion all along was that Jaeger was the last man in

the world to be meddling with Dickens—any more than such a one as Grosbeck should have been representing Keats—though of course in our business such anomalies are common. But for Jaeger to try to *be* Dickens, to write *like* him, seemed preposterous.

"Dickens?" he said, focussing on the word for a moment. "Well, yes—you are quite right. My effort to finish the novel was obviously futile. I did it simply as a sort of laboratory demonstration. But the basic *material* is of the utmost significance. To dismiss it as pedantic—" He tapped the envelope in his hand and roused himself to a better stance for lecturing. But then he took note of the envelope, turned it over, recollected his true position, and crumpled against the bench we were sitting on.

The afternoon continued hazy and very still, with a whiteness in the air. No one seemed to be about. An echoing rumble of city noise filled the space. The sun seemed to fade and recede, and an autumn chill settled over us.

"I tell you, Sanderling, I—I—"

"Come along back, Mark," I said. "It's getting cold. We can have a cup of coffee in the Union."

He knew I was trying to cajole him and he didn't let himself hear. He had immersed himself in his private grief.

The newspapers reported his death about a week later.

His wife came back from Anatolia and presented herself as an austere widow. Her dark medieval look added to the solemnities of the memorial service in the university chapel, but I think we all felt that she held us to blame for the tragedy. She was severe, almost fierce, in her austerity. She referred to her husband always as "Professor Jaeger." She spoke of his "unfinished work" with an implication of reproach, as though we had prevented him from doing it. In a more advanced culture such as Germany's, she suggested, he would have been accorded the highest recognition and honor.

And in a way perhaps she was right. We were deeply troubled and subdued and touched with guilt. We agreed to admire Jaeger more than we had in his lifetime. At the service appropriate lines from Browning's "Grammarian's Funeral" were read. "There'll be no one to keep us up to the mark," Dunlin was heard to say—and though the pun seemed at first frivolous it lingered in our minds.

"That darkness of utter despair," Medrick said in Shakespearean accents. "It is inconceivable to some minds, but there are times when all of us, sane as we may normally be, can experience it. 'To die—to sleep—'" He could make things like that sound appropriate.

CHAPTER 17

A TRUE RECORD OF our affairs would be a sequence of routines and monotonies. The happening, as it is now called, is rare. Classes, committees, conferences, exams, papers—day after day and year after year. It all merges inevitably into a continuum. As I think about it I tend to take nine-tenths of it for granted and to focus hopefully on the one-tenth that seems to offer some little chance for drama or humor, or even humanity. Jaeger's tragedy did occur, and does occur on other academic stages, but it is of course rare. There are McLoons and Grosbecks in the university world. There may be more Sanderlings—or there used to be. I remember how Simon Partridge took to me as a fellow countryman—he may even have said that we spoke the same language, as of course we did. Old-fashioned country innocence, as Jaeger had called it, is pretty much disappearing but it did once provide a sort of common denominator for us. Yet we go on doing the same things, going through the same yearly cycle; I think of it always as a great ferris wheel, beginning its first upward turn in September, and all of us in the one bucket, as it were, mounting and turning over the crest and falling toward the summer with the same inexorable pace as the revolving seasons.

I even think of each week as a small wheel, climbing from the low point of Monday upward and then over into Friday and down through the week's end. Routines go on like fate. The oddities and interruptions, the personal deaths and disasters, are all irrelevant. Perhaps all human worlds revolve in cycles, like the cosmic spheres, but I think the academic world is more obviously geared that way than any other. It is half aware of its old, old machinery that dates back to some remote medieval age in Bologna or Oxford, it goes through familiar rituals without quite knowing why or wherefore, it sustains visions of ideal detachment, it believes that wisdom is without date or current alteration. Many of us come to depend wholly on the academic cycles, great and small, to revolve us safely from boyhood to death.

Perhaps it is one of the half-awake dreams we cling to as long as we can, fending off the noises of actuality. Arthur Merlin, our poet, has written a darkly cynical poem called "The Tower," which describes the traditional ivory tower, where philosophers dream their dreams, in terms of an empty skull—presumably of one of our colleagues, though the evidence is too obscure to understand.

At all events, we are troubled by those noisy actualities. When Willett talks about the "new thinking" he voices our fear. We aren't up to the changes. It seems that unless we are new we are nothing—or at least we are ludicrous or impotent. We know that mathematics and physics and economics and linguistics and philosophy are all "new"; our colleagues in the School of Education tell us that effective teaching methods are new, and by definition ours are old and futile; our administrators (whom we never see and don't know) announce to the world that we are engaged in significant and challenging new educational break-throughs (I use their favorite vocabulary). And of course the students themselves are convinced that all this newness is a present reality: truth itself is new, as well as morality and sexual behavior. In every class, a few boys and girls aged say nineteen or twenty look at us with the cool bravado of a new emancipation: *we* are bound by nothing, they all but say; we can live, love, and die in ideal freedom, beyond your regulated restraints and legalized inhibitions; we choose to sit in this class only out of curiosity for the follies and dogmas of the long tragi-comedy of human history. In our own future, they say, all that will be changed, and we will demonstrate that peace and love and freedom are the only practicable virtues.

Few of us, I think, are really afraid of visions. We know how the "new" has always beckoned—we gear our philosophy and criticism to a recognition of the "new" in articulate men from Socrates onward. We are on the whole ready to be hopeful about any ideas that are brought forth from any source. Some of us (by "us" I mean my faculty colleagues, of course) are famous for advocating the new, and are seen with placards marching in demonstrations—young Max Eider, for one, our new linguistics man, has what the cynics call a Christ-complex, complete with poignant-looking beard, and leads processions in favor of love and peace. But we are full of uncertainty and scepticism. We are amused to see that Willett is always an advocate of new thinking and always dislikes and distrusts the new thinkers. Max Eider may be a nice guy, he says, but those whiskers are damned unsanitary and usually full of soup or egg: there really ought to be a law . . . .

But we have committees to review our methods and rec-ommend changes—all sorts of committees, of course, but chiefly one on the undergraduate curriculum for "majors" and one on the graduate programs. As an old-timer I have had experience on most of them, but of late I have been con-sidered less suited to graduate work and have been eased out of that area to make way for the sharper and more profes-sional younger men—and I must say that the new breed of scholar is a formidable type who operates more like a trained physicist than a traditional man of letters. I recognize in his presence that I'm not really with it. But I keep on with the committee for majors, and am now (as I write) the chair-man. It is my job to lead on into progress and change, to en-gineer what our vice-president calls a significant break-through.

But of course the whole problem is too dreary and con-fusing to try to explain. We have a language of our own, involving terms like distribution, concentration, language-options, related courses, honors, directed study, and so on—and it takes long experience to know what those and all the other terms really mean. There are complicated regu-lations and requirements, and essentially the issue is whether to preserve and strengthen the requirements or to abandon them—and as it happens our committee is balanced by two opposing attitudes: Medrick (the Old Pretender, Dunlin calls him, with a good deal of affection) is on one end (the right end, of course) and Max Eider is on the other. Dunlin rather goes along with Eider, but is incapable of taking any of it seriously. Bunting agrees that there is much to be said on both sides, though his habit is conservative. The chair-man, as usual, is somewhere in the middle with no ideas about a break-through in either direction.

Medrick is always reminiscent. He "goes back," as he says, with great delight—he talks about what happened at Chicago when Hutchins came in—

"A great figure," Eider says tensely. "Much too advanced for his time, of course: but unquestionably the foremost critic of higher education in America."

"Ah, yes—critic is clearly the operative word." Medrick's voice always has a rich round cellolike sound to it.

"He tried to set Chicago free—"

"Indeed he did. He almost wrecked it."

"He let in fresh air and light. He—"

"Ah, but I was there, you see, and you, I am sure, were not—unless still in swaddling clothes."

"Wreckage, as you call it, may be essential to any advance into new freedom."

"Wreckage, my dear boy, may also be a confession of failure. Is it not the child who destroys? The adult patiently amends and heals."

"Hear, hear," says Dunlin. "And two cheers for Thomas Hardy. But he was a very gloomy man, Hardy was. Do you think we can depend on him?" Dunlin makes it clear that he is up on Hardy, which the rest of us doubtless are not.

A committee doesn't get anywhere by such talk, but such talk is inevitable. Bunting breaks in to cite Whitehead as a sounder critic than Hutchins ever was, and gives us a one-minute review of Whitehead's theories. Medrick alludes rather grandly to the trivium and quadrivium of medieval educational philosophy. Eider cites the exciting advances made by Reed College in Oregon. Dunlin tells us about the famous general who became the president of a large university, and when he was offered honorary membership in Phi Beta Kappa he refused it because he was opposed to fraternities and secret societies.

The chairman steps in at this point and suggests that we get down to business. The question before us is whether all majors should be required to take a course in Bibliographical Methods—

"The question is," Eider says, "are we trying to turn them all into graduate-school specialists, or are we giving them genuine intellectual freedom?"

Bunting notes that it is not an either-or proposition. Method is essential to any intellectual activity. It doesn't preclude freedom, though he wonders what Max really means by freedom.

Our country, Max points out, was founded on the belief in freedom.

Bunting quotes Rousseau, and suggests that men are doomed to chains no matter what their hopes are.

Medrick moves that we recommend the course as a requirement for all juniors.

I inquire if he means it to be a year course or a half-year course.

Medrick says he had assumed it would be a year course, but now that I raise the question it seems more reasonable to stipulate a half year, to be offered in both semesters, perhaps, so that a student—

Dunlin interrupts to say that the title as now given is perfectly preposterous. Who wants to be required to take anything called Bibliographical Methods? It sounds positively pathological. Let's at least give it a charming name—let's call it the Junior Seminar. That doesn't commit us to much of anything . . . .

But in the end the old wrangle returns. Do we require, or do we simply offer? Our urbanity wears off. Max Eider is essentially a hot-blooded idealist, a utopian convinced that the only solution to all human ills is complete freedom. Let men be themselves, he says intensely. Let them *be*. Stop all this molding and brain-washing. What we are producing is generation after generation of robots, all designed to carry on and perpetuate the established System—

Medrick smiles with Olympian security. His beard, trimmed and brushed and shaped so elegantly, sets him above us.

Bunting, who has been visibly squirming under Eider's discourse, remarks that this kind of molding and brain-washing is exactly what goes on in Soviet Russia.

Eider's face is fairly well hidden under his biblical beard, but nonetheless we can see it turn pink. He is not trying to defend Soviet Russia, he says warmly, but it would be well to remember that it is we rather than they who have been most effectively brain-washed—

Bunting says that's all poppycock.

The chairman notes that there is a motion before us.

Eider insists that this issue is absolutely basic. Our entire educational policy, as a department and as a college, is reflected in exactly this kind of decision. If he could, he says, he would move that the whole ridiculous system of requirements and prerequisites and majors and minors and all the rest be eliminated and abandoned.

Dunlin calls out "hear, hear" and Medrick raises one of his kingly eyebrows. "You agree, do you? You also dwell in Arcadia?"

"Oh, it does sound delightful—don't you think? I see the lions and lambs all lying down together and everyone wandering about in an Eden-like landscape with a classical temple or two in the distance—" Dunlin sketches a pattern with his hand.

Bunting looks severely at me, and reminds us that there is still a motion before us. He agrees that it is a serious matter: as Max says, it is quite basic. He can't agree with anything else Max says, however. He regrets that Dunlin chooses to be frivolous about it—he notes that we have been sitting in committee for an hour and a half and are undoubtedly wasting our time. The issue is before us and he calls for the question.

But Dunlin is oddly annoyed at being called frivolous. No ideal vision is frivolous, he says. We are sustained by the thought of what we might be—

"More poppycock," Bunting says.

"Really, my dear fellow, there's no need to be ill-mannered about it. Let's at least pretend we are all scholars and gentlemen."

Medrick says the matter of the content and title of the proposed course has not been considered, and he would like to be sure of exactly what he is voting for.

The chairman points out that such a course is now being given by Professor Fulmar, and has proved very successful. The description and title are in the catalogue.

If it is to be *required*, though, Bunting notes, still red about the ears from Dunlin's attack on him, it will need more instructors and more sections—

More bureaucracy, Eider puts in.

More faculty salaries, Dunlin adds.

But the issue nonetheless, Medrick says, is whether or not it is desirable educational policy.

So in time the committee divides two and two and the chairman casts the deciding vote in favor of a required half-year course to be called the Junior Seminar. Bunting then points out that it isn't a seminar at all and do we really mean it to be a seminar—and is it to carry three hours of credit, or only two?

The chairman is somewhat embarrassed, but in a hasty series of decisions these matters are straightened out, the subject is considered officially closed, and the recommendation of the committee is ready to go before the Department as a whole—where, of course, the entire debate will be repeated, with suitable references to Hutchins, Whitehead, Rousseau, Socrates, and probably others.

When I meet Max Eider in the faculty room a few days later he speaks to me with forbearance. He is a very Christian young man, and I have a feeling that his kindly forgiveness is intended to heap coals of fire upon my head. He commends a book to me, *Mankind in Chains*, by Noah Zelinsky—he says it insistently, as though it should be considered required reading for elderly conservatives. He assumes, of course, that we really agree about most basic things like peace and equal rights and justice. It is obvious to all intelligent observers that our senators are controlled by the power interests, our president is a stooge, that our Latin American operations might as well be directed by Attila the Hun, that the truth about our dealings with Castro is too shameful to be told, that the only possible hope for political and social decency lies in the Free America movement founded by Professor Vole of Columbia, with chapters springing up in every major center throughout the country. Here at last, he says, is a formidable anti-establishment force, capable of challenging the entrenched power of the gangster-politicians who now control our country.

"Our university too?" I put in.

He recognizes my slyness and pauses for a nod and smile. I suppose he hardly owns a sense of humor, but he is very shrewd and has a debater's quickness of mind.

"As a matter of fact, yes," he says. "You will shake your head, of course, but a university like this is most certainly an instrument of entrenched and established power. It depends on the money it can raise from big business and on the patronage of the government; it dances to the tunes They play." His hand gestures off to the right to indicate where They lurk. "The trouble is, you see, that nice people like you don't really want to accept the obvious truth. We are actually the merest puppets in the hands of a predatory power which operates as ruthlessly as any fascism ever did."

I bring up Max Eider not to dispute with him or to imply any ironic detachment from him but simply to represent him. He is part of the record. I don't really try to answer him: I try to suggest that power must exist, it must exert itself, and some sort of They must be always at the center of it —and perhaps a Professor Vole of Columbia and his FRAM committee are capable of wielding it. I am of course sceptical. But Eider is not interested in my uncertain arguments. He simply assumes, and denounces. He writes letters to the student newspaper. He leads protest meetings. He opposes all new legislation in committees and faculty meetings. He leads groups with placards on the Common and pickets the State House and meetings of the School Committee and the City Council. His opponents accuse him of wicked intentions: he is subversive, a traitor, an enemy of decency, a publicity-hungry self-seeker—he is most often a son of a bitch; but in his own view of himself he is an honest idealist, willing to lay down his life for what he believes in.

"He's really a good teacher," Willett says. "But he's a pain in the neck. And we're stuck with him. There's not a damn thing we can do. If we fired him we'd be on every front page in the country."

⊷§ CHAPTER 18 §⊷

MY BEST FRIEND among these academic folk has always been John Piper and I suppose he is another old-fashioned country boy. He and Partridge and I formed a little nucleus in the department back in the earlier days, when things were simple and small and we represented a native New England way.

Not that we thought of it in those terms, or promoted ourselves with any such policy; we were merely on hand, we were the available local types. I can see clearly enough that we were, as critics like McLoon rather brutally point out, provincial and naïve, but of course I have an affection for that old way and I have a special affection for John Piper.

We both came as instructors back in the late twenties and for a couple of years shared a cheap furnished apartment in the neighborhood of the university—a fourth-floor walk-up. We lived a frugal and cautious life, and were probably happier than we have ever been since. Our habits were absurdly cheap, but full of innocent enthusiasms—a bargain-basement suit, for example, a big meal at Durgin and Park's old market dining room, second-balcony seats at a play—or far up under the roof of the opera house. We took trips in the old-fashioned way—a trolley to the Arboretum to see lilacs in spring, or a day's "sail" to Provincetown and back, or even to the wilder pleasures of Revere Beach with its carnivals and shooting galleries and thunderbolt roller coasters. We got on together with such unspoken harmony that we might have been married; our tastes, appetites, language, even our emotions, all seemed the same. I suppose we were untested; we lived inside a protective covering of social safety and simple-minded morality and frugal respectability. Our cheap little ways were comfortable, our pleasures were easy and safe, our innocence was impervious. We had almost no understanding of what was going on in the outer world, the political and social and psychological forces that were altering the whole course of human history.

I had my PhD then, but John Piper didn't, and he never went on to get it. Is it fair to say that he was even more innocent than I was? He was hardly touched by the realities of competition and professional status. His only aim for himself was to be a nice and conscientious man, and if he gave a course in Shakespeare, say, his whole effort was to be nice and conscientious about it. He was very respectful about all literature, and very modest.

But I see him mostly as he was in youth: even now I rarely take note of the pudgy and sagging man that he is, with his too eager habit of agreeing with everything I say. I see him as my old partner and shadow, almost my other self, taking the most spontaneous delight in the pleasures of plain living.

Partridge was of course a better, more able man. He had a commanding character, and became a power not only in the department but in the faculty as a whole—and the fact that he had no doctor's degree only enhanced his success. He was clearly a man to reckon with, regardless of degrees. He was older too, and since he approved of us and our home-grown background he was able to carry us along with him. In the stagnant times of the nineteen thirties our financial state was very low but we advanced in titles and rank. The department was stuck with us, and by the late forties when things were expanding and prospering we were solidly established and tenured. It is of course a problem in all faculties—how to avoid being stuck with well-meaning old timers. Even the vigorous Partridge was unsuited to the new academic culture, and as chairman for his last years embarrassed his younger colleagues—yet such a man can't be easily fired or pushed aside. In the end, as I said, they did ease Partridge out of his chairmanship, but it was a major and very difficult operation. As for John Piper, he simply faded away.

He handled the American lit for us, and back in the early thirties he did it all: a year's survey course, and various semester courses in special areas. I must try to explain that in the days of our youth American literature was regarded with affection as a sort of family affair: it was full of nostalgia and pleasant local idiosyncracy—and all Bostonians had proprietary connections with it. The dominant quality was quaint sentiment. The old scenes were full of charm—old farms, taverns, manses, old country dialects, old legends. It was easy pleasant stuff, we were told. It took no trained minds to read the great American poets, no explication of text, no scholarly scrutiny. All was simple and obvious—and inferior. No serious scholar paid much attention to it. The sophisticated student was somewhat embarrassed about it, and in the days of my graduate study at Harvard, for example, no one in his right mind would think of "doing work" in Melville, say, or even Hawthorne.

But John Piper grew up in the pleasant family atmosphere of New England literature. His father was a Congregational minister in Arlington, and read "Snow-Bound" aloud to the family every winter. He could quote the Biglow Papers on suitable occasions. He used Longfellow in his sermons. He had shaken hands with Oliver Wendell Holmes. He was related to the Jewetts of Maine—and John Piper has spent his life planning to write a major book on Sarah Orne Jewett, but is of course incapable of doing it: I'm afraid he is incapable of writing even an article about her, though he knows her work and life better than anyone.

With such a background John's courses used to be very pleasant, specially for those of similar habits. He had a following of schoolteachers and spinsters and librarians, all full of generous affection and good nature; they invited him to small gatherings, and he read aloud and told anecdotes about their favorite writers—in fact it is what he still does, and sometimes I go too and am surrounded by wonderful sentiment and approval.

But as far as modern scholarship goes, all this is preposterous. Our departments are now full of very serious specialists whose first article of faith is that American literature embodies profundities and mysteries; nothing is what it seems, and whatever is apparently pleasant and simple masks depths of frustration or tragic hypocrisy. No amateur reader can be trusted with Mark Twain, for example. It takes a trained staff of authorities. Hawthorne is hardly suitable for undergraduate reading, and is dealt with in the most advanced seminar. Everyone knows that Melville is difficult—he is to be understood only in the light of his infernal communications, as I heard one of our young men say at a colloquium recently. But Emerson is difficult too, and Thoreau is exceedingly difficult, and even Lowell is now recognized as difficult, and earnest articles and books are written on the Problem of Boston—or the Problem of Concord—or the Problem of Transcendentalism. A recent doctoral thesis has some such title as "Thoreau and the Phenomenological Illusion."

It is this kind of thing that makes the old-fashioned teacher feel like an imposter. The new men may be brought up to it: they learn, at least, to view these mysterious problems with poker-faced attention: like Mr. Walter Shandy they begin with the assumption that truth is concealed behind almost impregnable fastnesses, and only the most devious and subtle attack can begin to approach it. They know what a problem is even if they can't solve it. And of course there are always one or two among the new men who attack with such genius that wonderful insights are achieved. Only last year one of our men in Comparative Literature demonstrated that the key figure in all modern esthetics is Edgar Allan Poe—a "difficult" book (for me, at least) but unquestionably regarded as a break-through. It is called *Death and The Raven*, and received our faculty prize for the best publication of the year.

What really happened to John Piper has been the subject of a good deal of gossip and probably exaggeration, but apparently it was Jaeger who made academic life unbearable for him—with assists from McLoon and others. They were, for one example, on a committee to administer the undergraduate honors program, and in the heat of argument Jaeger used the phrase "incompetent sentimentalist" and went on to describe John's notion of advanced "honors work" as nothing more than the book-report system as practiced in junior high schools. McLoon was heard to mutter that he had been saying just that for ten years.

As I said, John Piper is as nice a man as ever lived, and his modesty is almost pathetic. When the semester ended he apologetically resigned.

Not that it was quite as easy as that. He had had sinus troubles that fall, and dragged along through the Christmas season with what he called the miseries, and finally the sense of his unworthiness grew almost unbearable.

"I'm not up to it, Sandy." He had a habit of nodding agreement with whatever was being said, including his own remarks. And he spoke with good cheer, even at the worst.

"Oh, it's the virus," I said, pretending I could jolly him along. "What you need is a better doctor. That old Goldthwaite of yours is a fossil—he gives you quinine water for everything that ails you."

He nodded and smiled in recognition of the old pleasantry.

"Christmas," I went on, "is enough to destroy the strongest among us. We do well to survive at all."

"No, no, it isn't that," he said, still nodding. "I do have this sinus condition—it is annoying and even discouraging, but—" He waved it away with a gesture. "It is no more, I am sure, than most of us are called upon to endure. You remember how Dean Briggs used to say that most of the world's work is done by people who feel miserable." He nodded in agreement. "Surely I can't complain. As soon as we have a few dry cold days I'll be much better."

"What's wrong, then? What do you mean, you aren't up to it? Up to what?"

I knew, of course, and I'm ashamed to say I was a little annoyed with him.

"It's simply that my work here is not up to what is expected in a university." He spoke the words helpfully, as though he were assuring me of a truth I should obviously have known.

But I went on being annoyed. "It's nonsense," I said. "You've been doing it well for nearly thirty years. Where did you get this notion, anyway?"

"No, no—I realize you are being too kind. You are a good friend, Sandy. You have really made my career possible—such as it is. Without you I should very likely be teaching in a country school somewhere."

"Oh, come on, John. Who's been talking to you, for heaven's sake?"

But he would only smile and shake his head with a half nodding motion to indicate that the whole thing was perfectly self-evident. It was embarrassing, he said, for a man with no degree and no publications to be representing a department that more and more prided itself on its professional scholarship.

"Embarrassing for whom?" I asked.

He never did come down to cases. No blame was to be cast upon anyone but himself. Any implied attack on him as unworthy and incompetent was quite obviously just. I tried everything—jest, anger, eloquence, cold logic. He smiled appreciatively, nodded with a characteristic sidewise motion, and reverted always to the plain fact of his failure as a scholar.

He meant to quit at once, and I realized that behind his mask of acquiescence was an almost choking unhappiness. He had to quit now—he couldn't inflict himself on us any more—he felt compelled.

"By the same reasoning I should quit too," I said. "Piper and Sanderling have always been partners, you know."

He laughed appreciatively at my jest.

So it finally came down to cajoling and insisting that quitting in the middle of the year was not fair to the rest of us—and at least he must stand in for another semester. He could listen to that kind of argument.

But from then on a visible change occurred in the appearance and habit of John Piper. He had always been a small and rather soft man, but in his prime he behaved briskly. He trotted up stairs. He nodded to all with quick energy. He addressed himself very earnestly to his professional business—in fact his conscientiousness was the basis of anecdotes, and jests and affectionate respect from many of his colleagues. We called him Honest John, and John Amend-All, and (with irony) Dear John, and when dismal jobs had to be done he did them: he dealt with the insoluble problems of transfer students, and for many years he and I worked on the sectioning of the large freshman and sophomore courses. He seemed, in fact, to take pleasure in such confusions, and devised all sorts of home-made arrangements for dealing with them, such as shoe-box files and charts tacked up on the back of his door. He could work half the night assembling statistics on class sizes and problems of scheduling and then deliver his results with an air of wonderful discovery and eagerness. I suppose he was merely a boy with a dream. Or, as I heard Dunlin say, a small beagle following the elusive scent of a non-existent rabbit. And when the dream passed, and he knew there was no rabbit after all, he seemed bewildered. He underwent a physical change. He softened and sank. He developed heart murmurs, and worried about his blood pressure. When he finished out that last semester and retired we saw him no more.

Not at public events, at least. But of course I kept in touch. His daughter Evelyn took faithful care of him—with some exasperation for his increasing helplessness. She remembered the times before her mother died, twenty years back, when he trotted so briskly, and he and she made a fine domestic team and life was in some mysterious way a pleasant adventure. She was happy enough to be his partner, if not his wife, and they went about together. Now he went nowhere—or almost nowhere. A few ladies from his old following sometimes cajoled him into a sentimental appearance at a club meeting, where he could read from the old poets or talk about the background of Sarah Orne Jewett's stories. But it was a question if the weather would allow him to go out at all, or if not the weather his sinuses or his blood pressure. He had trouble sleeping.

I drop in every week or two. Sometimes I walk over from my office in the mid-afternoon, a mile and a half or so—and then up two rather creaky flights of stairs to his apartment. It is by all modern standards a dismal place, with small windows, no sun, and a lot of brown woodwork, but it seems as secure and changeless as a castle tower. It closes itself off from everything, even air and light and sound. Except for a few electrical items, it is the same as it was when they moved in thirty years ago. "Those stairs," he says, nodding in agreement with himself, "are quite a problem. I have a slight murmur, you know—I'm advised not to undertake them more than once a day."

I try to joke about "old Goldthwaite" and he smiles his habitual agreement but the joke fizzles out. The airless silence of the place is smothering. I see a colored photograph of Ann Hathaway's cottage—it has been there on the same brown wall for thirty years. "Why don't you move?" I say. "You could get a place with an elevator."

He nods a little sidewise to indicate that I have a point.

"You need to shake yourself up," I say. "You're getting to

be a fossil. You crawl in here like a crustacean of some sort."

He laughs a little. I am obviously right. But no use to talk to him. He is what he is.

Evelyn blames us for destroying his career. She is not a bitter person, and not ordinarily unfair in her judgments—in fact I share her opinions about many things. "Couldn't you have *done something*, Sandy?"

She said it only the other day when I was there. We were having tea. John, of course, took no alcohol and no coffee (it was Harriet who changed my habits).

"After all," she went on, "you and he were in it together."

I wondered what would have happened to John if he had married a Harriet and learned to drink martinis. Could he have become less conscientious and more successful? I can't say that I thought of myself as successful, except in contrast to the sad decline of my old partner. His wife Edna had been a perfectly ineffectual and ignorant woman, but gifted with the kind of instincts that enabled her to surround and capture a John Piper. The old apartment was a memorial to her.

"Oh, it was my doing," he said. "We all know that."

"Nonsense, Father. You know exactly whose doing it was."

Again the nod, with deprecating shrug and smile. "No, no—we mustn't—that is, we can't put it on a personal basis." He made his voice humorous. He went through his little gesticulations.

"Oh, stuff! Don't think I don't know how they acted. That old buzzard McLoon, half drunk all the time—why don't they get after him? And Mark Jaeger." She faced round to me. "Well I don't care if he did—if he did—" She waved a hand. "He was really a dreadful man. You can feel sorry for him all you want, but I never could stand him. All he did was to make other people the victims of his own failures."

Evelyn, as I said, had always been a quiet kindly girl, very like her father, and the world considers her an inevitable spinster. The world, in fact, has been taught to despise or pity all virginal people—or to mock them. But Evelyn, like others, has achieved a balance among her forces that enables her to be steady and serene. I have known her since the day she was born, of course, and I should like nothing better than to have her in my house as daughter, companion, friend, immaculate partner.

Now she spoke out with more eloquent anger than usual, some of which she may have learned from Harriet who had said these same things many times.

"Evelyn doesn't quite realize," John was saying. "She doesn't see how the world is changing."

"Well, I know what human values are. Maybe that's what your changing world doesn't know." She went out to the kitchen with the tea tray.

"She realizes a great deal," I said.

His face had a collapsed look, and I saw almost for the first time that the old perky good will had gone. He used to be an image of benevolent intentions, an unpretentious Pickwickian, but now his indoor face had simply crumpled into age and sadness. He spoke without the mannerisms of good cheer. "Evelyn is very anxious to defend me, of course. She can't quite believe how much of a failure I have made of my career. I shouldn't be speaking of it, really—not even to my oldest friend. There's no profit in speaking of it, but Evelyn keeps insisting—even among other people. I would rather she didn't, but perhaps I am making too much of an issue of it. I can only wait things out. I must learn to be silent."

❧ CHAPTER 19 ❧

THE GOOD NOVEL, from a teacher's point of view, is the detective novel—or the murder novel. Long ago I read Aristotle. I learned about plot and characterization. Conflict, suspense, rising action, climax, reversal. And of course I learned about other tactics and amenities. In my youth style was the great thing, and style meant not only elegance and deftness but melodic grace and charm. Such qualities could be "taught," or at least set up as aims. A novel could be defined and charted like a trip over well-known terrain.

But all those things mean little or nothing to my students. Grace and charm are not their style; "English majors," as the vernacular has it, don't read murder stories, not even in secret, and mostly have contempt for them. If I note the professional skill and even brilliance in such work they make no response at all—except for an occasional arguer like Karsch who says all those novels are like the tract houses in the suburbs: the well-made house, he says with a quiet sneer, the well-made novel, story, play, picture . . . .

I say that people have to live in houses. There is some

virtue, I say, in anything well made.

But Karsch has no trouble with that sort of argument. Let the suppliers and purveyors go on operating—let them build and sell popular houses and popular amusements. The artist has an altogether different purpose and duty.

The Artist.

For the English majors, specially for the ones who "write," the artist, or more literally the recognized great writer, is the only divinity. Not that they worship or even like him—they are taught to be critical, and they don't really like much of anything—but they believe in the mystique of genius, and they believe that in art, specially in the very difficult art of our time, intimations of ultimate truth are to be found. Revelation is possible. The break-through is possible. No one can understand *Finnegans Wake*, no student at least, but that's where truth-beyond-truth may hide. Divinity itself is not to be mentioned, it is acceptably dead and gone, but the mystique is there, the something-beyond, the revelation that may supersede and even destroy all other revelations.

I speak of these rather arcane notions because I teach a course in writing, and every year I have to face a group of twelve or fifteen, each one of whom carries the seed of hope. He (or she) has no interest, or at least admits none, in writing for money or profit, or for supplying a market or providing entertainment—all that sort of thing is left to the commercial operators, the authors of murder stories and the builders of tract houses. He (or she) has been taught that the classic forms of art are mostly dead. The novel is dead—as is the well-made story and play. Also the sonnet and most of the other patterns of verse. And of course style, in the old sense, is dead. The only test is what you can get away with. And while those twelve or fifteen are outwardly quite modest and very punctilious about recognizing their own lack of talent and their folly in assuming they can ever be writers, they are all nonetheless the peers and associates of the world's great artists. They speak and think in the language of Faulkner and Joyce and Proust and Camus and Beckett.

It used to be a problem to me to know what I could teach them—given, of course, my own rather old-fashioned habits; of late years I have stopped trying to teach them anything. There are no subjects that can be usefully defined. Technique, like versification, is hardly a recognizable matter. Plot is of no interest to anyone. The word characterization has a quaint ring to it. What they write "about" is of course themselves. Each one plunges into his (or her) own youth—as of last year, say, or last month. Each is preoccupied with the problem of sexual lust. Each deals sternly or resentfully with parents and elders, including professors.

But of course it is foolish of me to generalize. Infinite variety exists even among twelve or fifteen. I see that the seeds of hope will inevitably die out, and the potential great artists will turn into mothers and fathers and teachers and what are generally called "intellectuals" by the news magazines. But perhaps one or two among them will have the persistence and luck—or the genius, whatever it may be—to go on and do wonders. It is always possible.

It was really Karsch who forced me to give up one of my old teaching gambits—and it may be that Karsch will be the ultimate genius among all of them. He has it in him, though he is not a man anyone could like. I used to read the familiar little story from Uncle Remus about Brer Rabbit and the Tar Baby—it took about ten minutes to read aloud, and I added a solemn professorial analysis of its technique. I pointed to its Aristotelian qualities as a classic comic drama, its brilliant characterizations of Brer Rabbit and Brer Fox as individuals as well as epic symbols, etc. Professors do talk this way, but not usually about Uncle Remus. I noted the build-up of the plot, the interrelationship of character and action, the crescendo of conflict through three stages (note on the mysterious effectiveness of three stages), the climax, the apparent defeat and destruction of the hero (I tossed in the word *hubris* here and there), the maintaining of suspense right up to the moment of reversal, the triumph of the hero, the vindication of a style and a way of life, the lyric finale . . . . For those who haven't read the story since they were nine, it might be worth the ten minutes or so.

But it won't do, not with Karsch on hand.

Obviously Uncle Remus himself is an insult to all people with a social conscience. Here of course the whole group erupted in argument, and the professor took a back seat. Uncle Remus, it seemed, was too embarrassing to be acceptable.

But as for those characters, Karsch went on, all you get is a good guy and a bad guy. That's the silly thing about all popular stuff—the hero versus villain routine. He went on to castigate the TV shows, the movies, and all westerns and murders. When I brought up Homer and Shakespeare and other ancient divinities he denounced the whole lot of them. They lived in simpler times, they had childish notions of heaven and hell, they were the world we had outgrown or outlived.

Karsch was a tough man to argue with because he could sneer with authority, and with a sort of wild and frenetic humor that enlisted the sympathy of listeners. "All this great literature bit," he said, "is mostly superstition—I mean like

Homer or like Milton or like Henry James." He never missed
a chance to assail Henry James, the cultural panty-waist, as
he called him. "Understand, they had what you call genius—some of them, like a gift, like the guy who can multi-
ply six figures—they could *write*. Even James—look at some
of those *sentences*, for God's sake. Or those chess players
with brains like computers. Or Mozart playing tunes—very
nice, I guess, if you like tunes. But we don't live there any
more. We live—I don't know where, and I don't like it, but I
know where we don't live, like we don't live where this creep
Uncle Remus lives or this other creep Isabel Archer
lives . . . ."

His discourses built up intensity like a rising siren, and I
felt obliged to interrupt and divert. The good guy–bad guy
cliché hardly applied to Brer Rabbit, I tried to say. It was a
rogue story, it was part of the picaresque tradition—

But of course I shouldn't have used any such word as tradition. This tradition bit, he called it. The ball and chain of
culture. Here were all these nice earnest naïve English
majors—he waved at his associates and chuckled almost
hysterically, he began actually to stutter in his excitement.
They studied Beowulf like crazy, and Chaucer like crazy, and
all those high priests and elders right down to *James*, and no
one ever told them that what they were really studying is
anthropology. He laughed as though he had uncovered a vast
joke. "I can respect scholarship as much as the next guy," he
said. "I'm all for digging up pots and busted statues, to—to
borrow a phrase—" He almost giggled. I made noises to interrupt, but he rushed on. "You get some curious stuff, all
right. John Bunyan, William Blake, W. B. Yeats—" He
waved a hand. "Crazy as coots. Percy Shelley, for God's sake.
How foolish can you get? Sure, it's all part of the old charade

and if anybody wants to study it that's fine with me—they can study fetishes and witch doctors and fossil bones. Why not? But do you realize that we so-called English majors, here in this college, in these classes, are supposed to take all this guff *seriously* as though it were *true*? I mean as though it had something to do with the world we are supposed to be living in. Great art, they keep telling us—it doesn't matter how remote, how crazy, how false it is, as long as it's somebody with a name like John Milton—"

One listener added "or Henry James" and some of the tension broke. But Karsch was not inclined to relish humor at his expense. He had a dark and angry look to him, his black hair came down over his eyes, and he stared at people with his mouth open in a snarling smile. "You guys let yourself be brain-washed, is the trouble. I think you profs do too. You go on saying these things year after year like a creed. In the beginning was Homer, and created he the Epic—and so on through all the Fathers and Sons—" By this time his smile had grown kindly and cheery—as far as it could. "I don't mean to insult you, Prof. I'm just trying to make out, so to speak. Our business here is to speak truth, isn't it?"

I agreed that it was. He did needle me, I must say, but I admired him. He turned in great quantities of manuscript, much of it incomprehensible to me, and I gave him a straight A grade. I had a feeling of sorrow about him too, perhaps because I couldn't see how he would ever fit into this or any other world. His vision of "truth" seemed to me too desperate to be endured. His writings were in part incomprehensible but what one did see was a cold and conscienceless evil in all human relations. A planned and persistent cynicism imbued every attitude. Was it a pose? Had he found a formula for astonishing his peers, as he might call them?

He was of course notorious among us. He objected to all our requirements, our complicated systems of courses and credits; he cut classes, missed exams, and quarreled with most of his instructors. In letters to the student paper he denounced almost every university operation from the president down to the food in the cafeteria. He attacked our Philosophy Department ("an ideal collection of Sunday School teachers"), our Art Department ("red barn enthusiasts"), and of course the English Department as the academy of what he called national pedantry. Or worse than that. He was good at insults. The Literary C.I.A., he called us. The Brain Washers. The Footnote Specialists. Our aim, he said, is Bibliographical Power.

Willett said he ought to be spanked. He's nothing but an unlicked adolescent, he said. What's the sense of being permissive about kids like that? If we go on letting him pour out insults and blasphemies there's no end to it. When I muttered something about his being a pretty brilliant fellow Willett's handsome face turned pink and he spoke strongly. "He's nothing but a pain in the ass," he said.

Grosbeck observed that some military discipline might improve him—and McLoon for his part added that it certainly would, it would kill him. Dialogues of this sort, I might note, were not direct: the two hardly spoke to each other, but exchanged opinions by issuing impersonal statements. McLoon went on to say that the only hope for a man like Karsch was to become a drunkard, like himself. Or perhaps a drug taker—and actually it looked to him as though Karsch were already hooked: his behavior seemed otherwise unaccountable.

Fulmar merely remarked that the young man was irresponsible and undisciplined, and had failed his Eighteenth Century course.

Max Eider, of course, rushed to his defense at every turn. He even wrote his own letters to the paper—not so much to endorse Karsch as to insist on his absolute right of free speech: but he suggested also that the university was obviously not much better than an academic concentration camp and it was high time someone said so.

Medrick observed that he was always amused by these young idiots. They have to grow up one way or another, he said. He had known Karsch ever since he was a freshman—the boy had made himself conspicuous the very first week. Give him credit for having brains, he said—he was really quite an exceptional lad. But you just have to be patient—give him his head, let him kick a bit. He'll settle down eventually . . . .

Settle down to what? I asked.

"Oh, discretion, I suppose." He waved spaciously.

"Doctor? Lawyer? Professor?"

"Ah, who can tell? He would surely make a stimulating schoolteacher."

It was Merlin, our poet, who recognized the genius in Karsch—he understood it and valued it. He gave Karsch A grades without qualification. But it seemed to me that he had almost nothing to do with Karsch. In a sense he had nothing to do with any of his students, even his closest disciples; he was preoccupied with his own life as a poet and celebrity—and I think he feared all rival talents. He went about in a quiet sort of trance, lofty and bland; he looked out at the world from a private stockade or keep where no one else ever came. But he knew, he understood what imaginative originality really was. Karsch had no discipline, of course, no idea of technical control—but as for *raw talent* . . . . I wondered how Merlin handled those Karschian polemics—in fact I was always curious as to how my colleagues operated behind the classroom doors. But Merlin was a secretive man.

It was Harley Coote who knew what went on, and who made fun of me for my Uncle Remus gambit. I haven't introduced Coote before now, probably because he is the kind of man you never clearly see. Dunlin called him our Secret Agent. Smallish, smoothish, gray-and-brownish—any age from thirty to sixty: a clerk, bank teller, cashier, even undertaker's assistant—all his qualities were neutral, as though he were designed to represent the national middle-class average. His job mainly was to handle foreign students and what is blandly referred to as remedial reading, but he filled in on elementary courses wherever it seemed necessary. No doctor's degree, no professorship—a department drudge and handyman: but he had the ideal qualifications for an international spy. He knew everything. He knew that Willett had once made love to Harriet, though he hadn't been here then at all. He knew all about Jaeger's sexual peculiarities. He knew that Grosbeck was a bad teacher. He knew what we all thought about each other, who were friends, who enemies, how we got along with our wives, what the deans and vice-presidents thought of us—he knew all about them too. He seemed to have a crew of student operatives who reported to him—they dropped into his small airless office at all times.

You'd say he was designed to be a blackmailer—at least there seemed to be no other useful purpose in his activity. But he did no one harm, and we all found him invaluable as an information center. If anyone knows, Coote will know—ask Coote—what does Coote say . . . . It was his vanity, I suppose, his academic one-upmanship: no status, no degree, a low-level hireling, but an indispensable part of our operations. A quiet man, with no compunctions about asking questions, or inviting answers.

"They tell me Karsch can be pretty obnoxious," he said. "Some of the students can't stand him, you know. They hope you'll jump on him. He's on drugs of some kind—he was arrested and fined last year. But it does give him status, he could have a following if he wanted, but he's a loner. Except for Rita—you know her, I suppose, the bloodless wonder as the boys call her. They live in a cellar over in the South End . . . ."

He could go on that way, with cheerful humor. Big items and little items all had the same value for him. I think he was pleased by all human activity. What did I think of Karsch as a writer? Merlin thought he was great, though he hated to admit it. Willett, of course, couldn't stand him.

In the end, anyway, I abandoned Brer Rabbit and the Tar Baby. Coote was not one to play up a joke with malicious intent—I suppose he could be called a low-keyed man, with a minimum of emotional energy, but he did manage to embarrass me about Uncle Remus. Dunlin exercised his wit on me—in fact for a few months I was addressed as Uncle by some of my more jovial colleagues. I might have stuck with it under other circumstances, but the Uncle Remus idea does lead to a sort of hysteria in these times. Karsch was probably right, at least about that. The story itself is good for another thousand years.

That, in a way, is where I do have to take a stand in teaching. In spite of effective sneers about tract houses and other duplications I am not able to abandon all that is useful or rational. Not long ago I had the notion of finding out how other teachers operate, and I visited one of my old students (as we say) who is now an eminent painter who conducts classes at Fenway School, where they pride themselves on being not only up to date but a few months ahead of the date. Levinson, his name is, and I asked him how he taught painting. I had some notion that he wouldn't be able to answer—that he'd simply say painting can't be taught (which is what teachers of writing say about writing), but he said at once that what he taught was Significant Form. Significant of what, I asked. It was a matter of Emotional Awareness, he said. He put these phrases in capitals as he pronounced them. The Language of Form, he went on, constantly impinges on us but like all the other dumb creatures of earth we don't really *see*. A curve, a mass, a juxtaposition of shapes, of color, all this becomes a Vocabulary.

I felt his enthusiasm. There was a visible glow about him as he spoke. He smoked a pipe. He wore dungarees and a blue sweatshirt.

"How about Symbolic Form?" I tentatively said.

"Oh, that. Yes, I see what you mean. Well, the question is—that is, once you get into symbolism you encounter other problems. Oh, it is vitally important—I grant you. Yes—yes, indeed." He made great play with his pipe. "There are symbols and symbols, of course. We in the Arts have to be pretty careful. We—" He sucked the cold pipe. "The question of representation is a tricky one, you realize that. We are really breaking new ground—here at the School we are exploring Form in ways that seem to us very—that is, very—er—fruitful. Symbolism so easily becomes didactic, you see. We have to be careful."

"Yes," I said. "I think I see. Meanings are often embarrassing, I suppose."

"Oh, it isn't so much that—though in a sense you are

right. At least, that's one way of putting it."

"How about coming and talking to my class," I said. "We need some good new ideas—I think we need to break new ground."

I couldn't seem to help a very small feeling of malice—I don't know why. I really thought a man like Levinson would be stimulating to my class, but I realized that with Karsch on hand there'd be trouble and I was curious to see what might happen. And I'd better say that I was probably a little jealous of Levinson's assurance, as well as suspicious of his theories. The paintings round about his studios at the school seemed to me nothing but dismal junk. But a man with convictions is formidable. He noted that writing and painting were discovering a good deal of common ground (I reminded him that of course Horace had noted the same thing, not to mention Lessing—and felt myself blushing a bit for being so unnecessarily snooty)—and he said he was of course terribly busy but he'd welcome a chance to come back to the old school and talk about some of his ideas.

And I must say that he stood up pretty well to Karsch. The rest of the class were really out of it. Karsch had no respect for what he called abstract esthetics, and lit into the Significant Form business pretty savagely. But Levinson was used to angry young artists. I had to admire him, though if I had to render a verdict I'd give the victory to Karsch. I tell myself that I don't really agree with him, but I see what he means.

CHAPTER 20

ONCE A YEAR OR SO someone is moved to write me about my old novel, *Aftermath*, which I published about thirty-five years ago. It still sits on public library shelves, and now and then some old-timer reads it. The reaction, if any, is reminiscent and nostalgic. I too, the letter says, lived up there—I remember it all, my grandmother behaved just like your grandmother. My Uncle Ernest tapped two hundred trees. I used to walk three miles to school at Upham Corners.

Nostalgia is what old country folk can't help. Peace and happiness were back there; life seemed to be what you made and did with your own hands. I never intended such a mood or motive in my novel, in fact I strove against it. It was necessary back in the early thirties to be harsh about all the conditions of life, to recognize that the farmer and the factory worker were both puppets in the hands of implacable circumstance. The New England farm was of course doomed anyway, but since the time of *Ethan Frome* and *Desire Under the Elms* it symbolized nothing but frustration and death.

That was supposed to be my mood in the novel. Not that I could hope to deal powerfully with such intensities and such lusts, but I saw my old family farm as pretty well lost and gone, and I tried to render it as candidly as my character permitted. Which in the light of the present, of course, is not very candid. I had a great many timidities about it, and felt obliged to change the characters and details so as not to offend anyone. It is all too bland and too plain, and I fear it has too much of what used to be called style—a sort of standard polite rhetoric demonstrating good manners and literary respectability. But I do stipulate that as novels of that type go it is better than you might expect: "better than likely," as country people used to say. I put off re-reading it for a long time; I thought it would be an embarrassment, like photographs of people in the preposterous costumes of older times. It does demonstrate that I was not qualified to deal with the lusts and hates of tragic drama: I can hear what such a critic as Karsch might say about it, though of course he wouldn't be hired to read it. Yet still, given all its limitations, it comes off, it has a life of its own, it makes a little world. The country affairs are plausible, the scenes are vivid enough (too much descriptive stuff, though), the mood is suitably sombre. What I was good at was the up-country dialect: I don't know why, but I had an ear for the native words and music of Vermont speech—at least I had it then. It still surprises me to read some of those dialogues.

But what I most remember about the job is the discouraging dreary labor of it—not labor so much as helpless frustration. I don't know what impelled me to keep on with it, to stare at the blank paper day after day, to write an uncertain line or two and then cross it out, to sit actually in a fixed waking dream, unable to control it or use it or escape it. A so-called day's work of writing left me in a state of nervous misery, vulnerable to ulcers, ill-tempered, convinced of the futility of all hope. The writing itself amounted to a dozen lines of script, along with another dozen or two crossed out and a good many marginal doodles. That was in my pre-Harriet life, and apparently I had infinite time to expend, and a one-track persistence that verged on folly. Once Harriet took over the direction of our affairs the whole enterprise of painful, dogged, ulcerous writing seemed to be out of the question. There simply wasn't time. And somehow there wasn't much point in it.

One thing that resulted from all this was a dream—I mean a real sleep-dream that recurs again and again. Harriet is bored by other people's dreams, and I am too: there's nothing more futile than having to listen to a literal rendering of a dream. So I never mention mine to her. But I have begun to recognize it as having some kind of insistent meaning, and since dreams do occasionally have great significance, in or out of literature, I've been thinking about this one of mine. Actually it sometimes occupies my imagination with such force that I recognize it as a demand. I must get to work on it, I must use it as the source and motive of the novel I've always wanted to write. It nags me. Yet as a motive it seems static and dreary and by now too old-fashioned to bother with. Everything about it is gone and forgotten.

I had an Aunt Martha who lived on a back street of Allensville, alone in a two-story village house—a white clapboard house among other white clapboard houses. Aunt Martha herself was white—her skin, her hair, even her clothes, were always white. Her eyes were pale blue. I thought she was the nicest woman who ever lived, and I think so still. When my sisters and I were taken to see her she blossomed with smiles and eager generous impulses. She had a party for us, with lemonade and sugar cookies and cake; we sat at her dining table and had napkins and plates; she brought treasures from upstairs, old, old dolls, and miniature furniture, a crib, a bed, a bureau with drawers. They came from some old time long before her own childhood. It was all a ritual, and we were subdued and impressed. The house was full of old things too, never to be moved or altered; the unused parlor was cold and smelled of mildew—I looked in and out quickly as part of the ritual of the visit. She wanted us to feel at home, she said; she wanted us to do whatever we liked. She said very little, actually, nor did she yearn for us sentimentally like other lone women, but her kindliness somehow enveloped us. When she was amused she didn't laugh but made a little twisting gesture with her head, and sometimes quick flushes of pleasure came in her white cheeks.

But with all her sweet half-timid kindness, I remember her as sad. Her stillness was sad, and her shyness. She stood in a doorway watching us, ready to wait on us, to fetch cookies or toys; she smiled slightly and twisted her head with humor, and a faint color came in her white high-boned cheeks; I felt an almost physical impulse of love for her as though she were a young girl whom I could touch. I feel it even now, a half century later. I must have been ten or so then. She had a slim waist and walked lightly. But she was sad, I knew, and somehow lost. She lived by herself in that big village house, with a closed-off parlor and all the upstairs rooms unused, and the attic, and the sheds behind and the barn.

She'd ought to sell it, people said. She'd ought to go and live with her daughter in Ohio. I used to hear them, my grandmother and the other old ones, and they kept repeating it: she'd ought to clear out of that old house, it wasn't right for a woman like her. Lucky she had neighbors to help her out, but even so—even so— Voices were sad on her behalf, and a little indignant: she had no business being a lorn widow clinging to an old house and an old life. Oil lamps, I remember, and wood-burning stoves, and for plumbing a hand pump at the kitchen sink. I never went there in winter, but they told how hard it was.

That's how my dream began, but little by little it took on motives and emotions of its own. Aunt Martha's white house was a fine specimen of Vermont classic, built actually by Uncle Dan's grandfather, about 1810. Even to me it has seemed that our New England origins belong to a time infinitely remote. In my boyhood everything was said to be a hundred years old, houses, furniture, all properties: I can hear people saying it over and over. Oh, it's been there for a hundred years. And to a child that's the same as forever. To think of one of the old houses as actually having been built by someone's remembered grandfather was almost an impossibility. The very look of the houses removed them from time. To me as I grew up, and even now, what we call a colonial house belongs to the infinity of history, like a medieval church or even an ancient temple. Uncle Dan's grandfather belonged, so far as my imagination went, with the Caesars. The house itself could never have been "new": even in 1810, a "hundred years ago," it must have appeared somehow as a venerable classic.

These illusions are specially strong in my generation. My elders took all the old stuff pretty much for granted. My grandparents could see those houses and ways as still young; Aunt Martha continued to live in "her house" where she naturally belonged. But I did grow up in a new kind of world, as everyone knows. The old stuff was pushed back and away and for a while was half forgotten or even despised. And then in the twenties came the sentimental re-discovery of it all, and the revivals and imitations, and finally a larger philosophical perspective. Early New England, like early Greece, was seen as a cultural matrix.

And there, in my mind and dream, the house still is, waiting for me to come back to. And it is endowed with mystic and poignant meaning. The whiteness of it is unlike anything on earth, the old pure whiteness of sun-dusted clapboards, and the Doric order of the front door and moldings of the cornice. All the houses along the street stand in the same white silence, under great silent elms—bare of leaves, for a cold sunlight comes through and washes over all the surfaces, a light without much shadow. I know that Aunt Martha is in there, waiting in the stillness—I am outside in the street somewhere but I can see her white face and her white hair pulled back tight on each side of a part. I have a sense of coming home at last, of reaching the end of a life's quest. Here it is, the serene good place, the pure house, the pure life, the sweet and immaculate woman waiting to take me in. This is what I have lived for and yearned for all these years—this actually is what mankind lives for and yearns for.

But the vision is overwhelmingly poignant. In my sleep I am crying. It is all pure and beautiful in its whiteness, but it is lost, lost, lost. Aunt Martha is so forlorn and alone that I can't reach her—I only see her there inside, through the walls. I see the old things around her, all fixed in silence, the chill damp parlor, horse-hair chairs, sideboards, spool beds in the unused rooms, one massive rope-corded bed with hand-turned posts—I know somehow that everything is cold.

And no one walks on the street, nothing moves or makes

any sound. I am there, standing, but almost disembodied. I recognize that I have come at last after long and hopeless searching and I know that this is it; and of course I am profoundly gratified, I have a sense of recognition and fulfilment as though I finally know what I live for. But above all that is the agonizing sense of loss. All hope, desire, youth, beauty, all dream of whatever is pure and perfect in life—all comes to this.

I wake with a face wet from tears.

I am annoyed at the expense of emotion. I think of how useless and irrelevant my dream is. I try to dismiss it as sentimental. I make an effort to think realistically about old houses and the old life. That mildewed parlor, I think. The drafty out-house off at the far end of the sheds—I always wondered how my immaculate aunt could have made herself use it. I think of the house as it must be now, with unknown people in it, rather shabby, a junk car in the yard, a TV antenna on the roof. The great elms are dying.

But in some buried part of me the dream is unquenchable. It keeps coming back. The emotion of it is both oppressive and cathartic; I wake with a sense of tragedy. It makes me feel that life can be mysteriously rich and strange. All dreams do that, of course—and perhaps that is what they are for. But this one has a poignant dramatic logic to it.

But I suppose in Harriet's opinion I am indulging myself shamefully. She is a New Englander too, and her family like mine once had country connections. She created our house with the old images in her mind, and sometimes in my dream I half-include this house as well as Aunt Martha's, in the sort of visionary confusion that is natural in dreams. She is pleased with the charm of it, of course, but looks on it as she would look on any pleasing design; the house is a kind of personal victory for her, and represents a subtle and clever modernization. Harriet is not given to backward yearnings and illusions.

Nor am I, really—at least I try to take a reasonable view of the possibilities of life. I must after all face up to Karsch. And others as well, with other illusions. I see that John Piper really failed, he was found wanting; and I see that Simon Partridge came close to failure, in spite of his great strength. They didn't really listen to what others were trying to say.

But failure is an easy word to use. My young students, as I have said, apply it to all sorts of characters with almost supercilious confidence; they seem to assume that the purpose of serious literature is to chronicle human failure, from Oedipus, say, to Leopold Bloom or the more recent anti-heroes. They assume that if the truth were told about any-one, it would be in terms of failure. They learn this attitude from the higher criticism they read and from the professors who teach them: it is one of the basic assumptions, at least in the arts. I must agree that such a one as John Piper is a failure, not so much because he has neglected his scholarship and contemporary criticism as because he is full of a miserable sense of his own inadequacy in his profession. Nothing is much worse than that. But Partridge is still sustained by a well-founded belief in his virtues and successes. The arrogant critic (or student) may disdain him as one of the failures, but I've seldom known a happier man. He may not experience any such operatic dream as mine of the white house, but he has recovered his ancestral virtues, with suitable modern conveniences, and lives in terms of them. He has "come home"—at least I am pretty sure he has. In the end what seems to count most is the dream, the half-unconscious sense of living out a rôle that has been prepared for you in some other world than this. You feel it even when you wake in bed after the vaguest intimations. Sometimes you live within it most of the time.

We three, anyway, have been the old country-boys of the department; we have represented the early provincialism of New England education—though perhaps other words could be used: puritanism (a hostile word now), Victorianism (absurd these many years), perhaps a touch of the genteel tradition, though that implies more wealth than we ever associated with. I can't help my dreams and my sub-conscious yearnings, nor can I imagine my life without them, but I do make some effort to face up to other things too, as I said.

◄§ CHAPTER 21 §►

A LETTER HAS COME addressed to Professor Robert Sanderling, Emeritus. It is from the state Department of Education, and invites a recommendation for one of my former students. It is the kind of thing I've been getting for thirty years or more, but the Emeritus is new to me, and a shock.

I began this remembrance of our departmental affairs three or four years ago and have added to it unsystematically, looking ahead to that still distant time, as I thought, when the finality of retirement would occur. I have dreaded it for no very cogent reason, except that I cling blindly to my habits. I think of retirement as a sort of drifting off into darkness, with no return. A pusillanimous view, unlike the stalwart Partridges, for example. So, except for a nagging concern about the required farewell speech, I have refused to face the fact. Some day I must utter the fateful words "friends and colleagues," of course, and some day I must go home to Harriet and stay, but the date has always hovered off in the unmeasured future.

But now Emeritus. It is what they call you after sixty-five.

And somehow it got on the official docket of the Department of Education.

One more year of teaching. I am appointed to it. All the old arrangements are over—the tenure, the pension deductions, the health plans. And next spring, probably in April, there will be the little farewell observations, the luncheon, the kind sentiments, the modest gift.

It strikes me with a small feeling of unworthiness that after all these years here I have almost no close friends. John Piper is one, of course, though I have felt sad about him since he dropped out. But he is unquestionably my friend, as far as an old man may have a friend. It is apparent to me, though, that old men, even semi-old men, don't have friends—not in the way they did in their days of hope and youth. Young people, I believe, hardly realize that they are alone in their lives; they are beguiled and entertained in effective groups or partnerships—they act together. When they little by little give up acting, as we all do, the partnerships dissolve. The musketeers turn into rather absurd middle-aged citizens with family troubles. But we can use the word friends in a very loose and convenient sense: we mean the people we call by first names, whose houses we dine in or drink in, whom we greet with kindly jests. My colleagues are nearly all friendly and generous men. I can ask them for help or expect help to be offered. One year I was too ill to teach for the last two months of a semester, and John Piper stepped in to carry one of my courses, as you would naturally expect, but it was Mark Jaeger, much younger then, and at the peak of his arrogance, who took another—and though it was evident that he disapproved of my whole approach he did the work with perfect good will. Many such troubles occur to all of us. We have intellectual and professional differences that flare up into fierce quarrels, but in human terms we do pretty well. Willett may mutter profanely about this or that bastard who doesn't represent his notion of a scholar and gentleman, but he administers scrupulously and generously, and defends all his young men against attacks from any source. The college teacher is basically committed to promoting civilized behavior, however he may define it, and he quite often tries to live up to his visions.

It isn't friendship in the idyllic sense that it seems to be in youth. The only hedge an old man has against supreme aloneness is his family, and often enough duty rather than affection governs. I can live with Harriet partly because we are assigned to each other, and because we have a house and a routine and a bank account and we know where we are, and partly because we have twisted and tied ourselves together for thirty years. If we met as strangers now we would not be friends, obviously, or partners in anything, but there's no doubt that we are as interdependent as twin beech trees that have grown into each other. Marriage. A hedge against unbearable solitude. More than that, of course: a function, an activity, a duty, sometimes an achievement—as I think ours is. I wonder sometimes if Harriet were to die whether Evelyn Piper would want to marry me—I speculate about the possibility with an absurd sort of detachment. Evelyn is not quite forty yet. We'd have to have John too, which makes the whole idea even more absurd. If I die, Harriet will become an old witch—I can see her as a more and more notorious Character in the neighborhood; but she will do well in that rôle—she has a talent for existing alone.

I think of Joan, really, as my truest friend. I am sustained by that dream. When all else is dead and gone, and I am faced with hopeless solitude, Joan will be there—not in duty but in spontaneous companionship. And Joan's sons will recognize not only the titles and status of their aged grandparent but will see him as lovable and even charming.

That's how old men feel, anyway. But if they have any wisdom they will learn the art of being alone—and being alone in weakness. There's no more adventure, not very much brisk self-reliance, nothing but a mind functioning. And at the last merely an instinct.

Colleagues—and friends. Perhaps others have more talent for friendship than I do. I have a sense of the intimacy of other men—I see them going off to lunch together, or arranging for theatre tickets, or even trips to Greece or Italy, with wives. I probably have twinges of envy: why am I not urged to have lunch or go to Greece? I tell myself that if I really wanted such pleasures I would act and arrange: it is futile to wait passively to be asked. You think little, Sanderling—you don't, in other words, command and direct your destinies. You stand by, you are passive—that's your way. I know all this better than McLoon does, but nonetheless I am envious at the thought of boon companions at Delphi together. Perhaps I am really envious about all sorts of things—like the lovely generous-hearted girls that have never been mine, or the rich cultural elegance of the Medricks, or the academic successes of my associates. As I slip out of my office in midafternoon and head off for a small solitary venture down town I am probably contented enough, and even complacent, but I am also the sixth grader slipping away from school because he is not good at sports and is afraid to face up to this or that group or gang. It begins as a retreat and a kind of failure, but after a long lifetime it becomes a way or a style, with philosophical acceptance and perhaps justification.

I reflect about it not to defend, but to make clear. Teach-

ers, bookish people, are more often than not the ones who
slip away—because of inability, or distaste, or cowardice: but
in the end, if they are lucky and deserving, they may achieve
other kinds of courage—or wisdom.

When I do make that little farewell speech I think I'd like
to say some things I've never said before. I still imagine
myself speaking, beginning it, with what I hope are appropriate jests. At last, I say, I intend to read some of the books
I've been lecturing about these forty years. I'm not good at
funny stories, of course, but then I'm not very good at serious
pronouncements either. When I try to formulate ideas, as
thinking men do, I end up with embarrassing clichés. Ideas
themselves are almost never new, but style can be new, and
relevance and appropriate drama can give old ideas new life.
I always admire the ones who can think and speak effectively on their feet, as Partridge could, or Medrick. My own
recourse is to mumble and flounder among too obvious
truths on the one hand and evasive ironies on the other.

The academic freedom we have enjoyed all these years—is
that worth taking note of? Is it actually an illusion? No one
has ever told me what to teach or how to teach, except in the
general designation of the larger subject matter. No inspector
or administrative spy has ever slipped into a back row of a
class to see what I was up to. No investigating committee has
summoned me to account for myself. A teacher, I think, can
only be grateful for such freedom. But he might be a better
teacher if he had some advice, or even coercion. And
then—how far may he push his freedom? At what point does
the administration begin to be uneasy and think of the
dangers and limits of freedom? No one, the honest philosopher always realizes, is free; the limits exist, whether we recognize them or not. The real question is always where to

draw the lines and admit the limits.

But what I must say to my colleagues is that I am grateful for this generous scope of freedom. With less freedom we would be so much the less men—that is, our thinking would be constrained, evaluations would conform, we would be less individualistic and less interesting. We have, I think, struck a good balance, we have managed to draw the lines in the right place. As for the ones who demand more, always more—I am not one of them, of course, as everybody can plainly see, but without them we'd be a complacent lot; we would take our freedoms and prerogatives for granted, we would slip back into self-congratulation. They keep us looking in the right direction.

May I say these things? Is there any use in trying to say them? My only notion, really, is to do justice to a profession that has been undervalued or at best simply taken for granted. Some individuals may attain greater usefulness and self-reliance—a few writers and artists, say, or a contemporary Thoreau or two—but the profession of college teaching, at least as I have known it, stands high. In what other field may a man honestly consider himself on equal and argumentative terms with the sages and masters of all human culture?

I imagine myself speaking of integrity too. I can't assume that my colleagues possess it above all others, but I can testify that in spite of all vanities and all conceivable exasperations, we believe in it very strongly. Perhaps we sometimes protest too much about it, or about the forms and evidences of it. The research professor parades his scruples; he lets it be known that his findings and conclusions are founded on the bed-rock of primary evidence, and that all his thinking is as unassailable as a nuclear physicist's. As we face up to our doctoral affairs we are more like physicians than literary humanists—I can always hear Willett's "on the doctoral level" like a call to the highest duty. But a too manifest professional integrity is better than too little, and my irony on the subject is largely a reflection of my own inadequacies.

In small affairs too we get along with mutual trust. In the years I have had to do with promotions and appointments, on committees formal or informal, I have seldom been aware of meanness or personal enmity. We speak as well as possible of every man. It is necessary to fire young men, and not because of their failures. It is necessary too to select those to be advanced, and there also many considerations rise. Choosing is the hard problem, and all debates are carried on conscientiously. If prejudice appears, it has to withstand some pretty outspoken scrutiny.

I shouldn't be lecturing about these things. That's the trouble—that's why I have no confidence in the speech I'd like to make.

And what of our real function as teachers? What do we accomplish—and what could we?

May I speak about this at all? Is it too serious? Or simply too impossible?

It is not, of course, too serious for some occasions—a Phi Beta Kappa address, say, or an article for *The American Scholar*; but after a farewell luncheon the mood is light and mellow. And I'm not the one to evolve new theories. I push along the familiar ways, moving through the weeks and semesters and years, doing the things I've always done, hoping to do them as well and usefully as possible. But I'd like to be able to say that we do bury ourselves under routine and professionalism. We function more in terms of what we accept as the scholarly tradition than of the human individuals who face us day after day. For some of us scholarship is a dogma and ritual, to be accepted as an established doctrine of almost ecclesiastical rigidity. Professor Grosbeck, I am told, spends the first two hours of his course on the Romantic Poets on bibliography—and if I ever had the temerity to challenge him on that I am sure he could defend and justify his method with powerful effect. Denigrating the methods of scholars is a game for dilettantes, and perhaps I'd better be quiet about it. Yet the poetry, as far as Grosbeck deals with it, remains simply a "corpus," a body of literary and historic data.

It is obvious that I would not be brave enough to say this in his presence. I remember one of our graduate students some years ago turning against us in almost hysterical anger. "*You all hate* poetry. *You hate* novels and drama. You merely use all that stuff as a means to professional advancement—and you wish you didn't have to. You'd rather drink bourbon and read murder stories."

But I suppose the old-line scholars are outnumbered by the new critical analysts, and we have those too, like Dunlin for one, or Bunting with his difficult book on Wallace Stevens. Their intention is to find esoteric meanings, to devote themselves to sexual repression in Hawthorne, or the use of the mandala symbol in Faulkner. In a way it is the tide of our time, it is what is happening—in the arts and in all behavior: the only possible advance is toward complexity, or, to put it more simply, toward the discovery of new complications. Nothing can any longer be what it seems to be. Dickens may not be understood without an analysis of his vocabulary—preferably with the aid of a computer. Butler's satire on the absurdities of English culture is an aspect of his homosexuality.

Of course there's no point in my saying these things—and

they aren't effective anyway. What I really have in mind, and what I would like to say, is that it is the main business of teachers on any level, and specially of teachers of what we call the liberal arts, to be humane—or perhaps I should say humanistic. This above all the rest. We are people trying to learn to live well, or live right; the students who face us in the classrooms are more uncertain about it than we are, and in the flux of our times they are willing to look at and consider any truth, any vision or solution or achievement, any light from any source.

I could perhaps say something of this kind, but it would come out too seriously—and too obviously. It would sound as though I were questioning the right of my colleagues to be professional—and probably it would lead to muttered comments about the old fallacies of using English "to teach about life." English is to be cherished as one of the major intellectual disciplines. And teaching about life inevitably bogs down in half-baked personal philosophies that have no relevance to a competent knowledge of the literature itself. We all remember the eager young teachers of Freshman English who have used their classes as sounding boards for their own social gospels.

So in the end—caution, compromise: much is to be said on both sides. Teaching, like art, like truth itself, is a resolution of many forces and claims.

Meanwhile in this last year I have more and more a sense of detachment—not only from the affairs of the department but from everything. I walk about like a returned spirit, observing things but not quite taking part in them, as though I were almost invisible. I say "almost" because I am actually seen, and spoken to, yet I feel less conspicuous, even less solid—I feel somehow in an evanescent state like the Cheshire Cat. I can at least smile to the end, and in fact I find myself smiling much more readily, with a guilty sense of irresponsibility. I am on no committees. I go to no faculty meetings. I take a bland and frivolous view of the crises and rumors of crises that confront my colleagues.

If all this sounds in some ways pleasant it is also an aspect of weariness. I walk about as briskly as I ever did, and can stand up to an hour's class—or longer—with energy, but there seems to be a slight inner malaise, an impulse to give up. I resist it, I take note of my brisk elders, like Partridge, or one of our celebrated retired philosophers named Albert Hopper who at eighty-seven is still invited to teach a seminar: he is as pleased with himself as a child of eight. If I am to live, I tell myself, I might as well do it briskly. But the spirit has its own mysterious ways and is not amenable to rational advice. Giving oneself pep talks at the age of sixty-six (going on sixty-seven) is very necessary, I find, but it doesn't bring the results one hopes for. A persistent half-audible voice keeps suggesting that in the end the struggle avails nothing.

But Harriet seems to be growing brisker. She has decided to be a sculptor and has fixed up a little back pantry for the work: at least that was how she started. But what she is doing is a sort of creative carpentry, and she overflows through the kitchen and back hall. She assembles wooden bits and pieces, nails and glues them into odd shapes, paints them, sets them up on shelves and tables. She pretends not to be serious, and is full of sardonic ironies about her custom-designed junk, but lately she has devoted all her energies to it. She scours the local region to collect mill scraps, bits of moldings and turnings and anglings—she keeps boxes of them in all available corners. She operates power tools, spe-

cially a sabre-saw which just suits her character (as she says).
And she is branching out into fame—she has "shown" at two
or three art stores and galleries. "Go right ahead and retire,"
she says. "I'll be famous and rich before you know it. Esthetic junk—people seem to love it." She talks as though the
whole thing were preposterous, but she is more and more
enmeshed in it; the "people who love it" seem to be three or
four new companions less than half her age who drop in for
drinks: one of them writes art notes for a Boston newspaper,
and manages to allude to her work with implications of great
respect and significance. "The Dimensional Sculptures by
Harriet Sanderling," he writes, "reveal a refreshing new approach . . . ."

But what this led to, for us, was one of those grinding
matrimonial quarrels which suddenly destroy all security and
peace. "Approach," I had facetiously said, is the wrong word.
In view of the materials and methods, wouldn't "break-
through" be better?

That's her kind of humor, I thought. The slightly sardonic
irony—except that she objects to puns. I don't know why,
unless it is because she has never liked the kind of people
who make puns—who look at you, she says, expecting applause. I learned that long ago. Not that I ever had the habit,
not compulsively, at least, but I used to argue in class that
the pun at its best was the highest form of humor. But actually I don't think it was my word-play that touched off her
resentment—it was the basic question of her art.

"What you'd prefer, I realize," she said, "is a cherub for a
garden fountain. That's about your level of art. A cherub
with dimples."

"Well," I said too recklessly, "I've seen some pretty nice
cherubs—"

"And you're the man," she went on, "who is supposed to

be teaching *creative writing*, for God's sake, in a university. They might just as well have had your old Aunt Martha. Don't they *know* what kind of a character you are?"

"Not apparently as well as you do," I said.

"They're all petrified and fossilized, that's been obvious for quite a while. Look at the deadwood—look at the Sanderlings and Medricks and Willetts—"

"Willett," I said. "I thought he was your boy."

It was the first time any such thing had been mentioned between us.

"What the hell do you mean—*my boy?*"

"Well, he was once, I suppose."

"Now just fancy that. Willett, my darling old varsity cream-puff. Christ, Sanderling, you really are a one of a kind. Don't tell me you've been brooding all these thirty-odd years about me and Willett?"

"You don't really have to put on an act, Harriet," I said. "It doesn't matter all that; it never did."

"Well, just let me tell you a few home truths, my poor futile spouse . . . ."

Agony. Bottomless misery. No sleep, sharp pains in the gut.

It happened that this domestic misery came just a few days before the departmental lunch I had been anticipating for ten years. And my turn arrived, as I had visualized so graphically. The long table, the familiar faces, all affable and tolerant, the little displays of wit: Willett at the head, I at his right. Medrick handsomely at his left, the others all at random, including younger men I hardly knew—a couple of younger women too.

"We are here to tell Sandy how much we like him and admire him . . . ."

The varsity cream-puff, I thought, hearing her raspy words.

He smiled as he spoke. His eagerness was very genuine. He stood straight and somehow lightly on his feet, still the young athlete, with English tweed jacket, button-down shirt, subdued tie. Pleasant to see, and sincere.

A fine cowhide briefcase, with initials and brass trimmings. Many friendly jests about my dilapidated old one, which was apparently more conspicuous and amusing than I had realized.

Then the silence, the expectations.

"Friends and colleagues."

I felt the hollow below my stomach, the splintery little aches, the head buzzing and pounding. Stumbling words—sincerest thanks, fine colleagues, fine friends. Regret at parting, pleasure at prospect of more leisure. No mention of "doing my own work." No mention of efforts to compose a memoir—certainly no mention of that. "I intend at last to read some of the books I've been lecturing about these forty years." Pleasant laughter all round. "Hear, hear."

I am sitting down. I hear the buzz and rustle of conversation. I've said nothing worth saying. But it is over. It is my last public speech.

"The old routine, I suppose," Harriet said when I got home. We had agreed on a truce. We shared martinis. She noted the splendid briefcase. "It's a little late in life for that—but cheers anyway. You can load it up with murders at the Public Library. Did you make a nice speech?"

"Perhaps it was nice. I didn't say anything worth saying."

"Well, of course not. You didn't expect to, did you?"

I took a swallow and looked at my glass.

"It was a nice occasion, I'm sure," she said. "They meant well. You meant well—what more can you ask?"

◄§ CHAPTER 22 §►

My ACTIVE connection with the department pretty much ends there—or at least I assumed that it would end there. I went home in a mild trance, as though I were waiting for an anaesthetic to take effect, or even some sort of preliminary death. Not that I intended to be dramatic about such low-keyed affairs. As Harriet noted, it was a routine. It is all written, as old fatalists used to say. And I had had plenty of time to prepare both heart and mind.

What some of my feelings settled down to was simply guilt, or regret. Life had come, offered itself, and gone, and I had rejected—not all but much of it. I think almost all men feel this way, and I am sure it is never very clear to anyone what exactly it is that we reject—or accept. Is it that mysterious veiled bride "Opportunity" that Conrad evokes in *Lord Jim?* Anyway, I did regret. I had simply done too little, had been lazy and passive, had succumbed to a too easy routine. I had written one mediocre book early in life and had never summoned up will or energy to do another—unless these rather random reflections can be considered "another." But as far as

scholarship is concerned, or criticism or any sort of intellectual commentary, I have hardly justified myself. I can see
that some of my colleagues have also done very little; I remember too vividly the tragedy of Mark Jaeger, and I know
how that sort of frustration gnaws at the vitals of most of us.
Probably, Grosbeck is the only man in the whole group who
is unbothered by a sense of failure. We all live in a condition
of pressure, not so much because we must "publish" to hold
our jobs and better our rank as because we think we must
justify our professorial existence: Other men, the young men,
come along and perform scholarly wonders, and are seen to
be a new breed of genius, with new visions and new truths.
The rest of us slip back, fade away, are delegated finally to in-
significance and oblivion.

Perhaps all human aspiration invites the same personal
ordeal: the spectrum of success and failure exists in every en-
deavor, and almost every contestant is aware that he hasn't
lived up to his hopes and promises. But scholars, as I have
said, compete in a very big league. They measure themselves
not only against each other but against Aristotle and Lucre-
tius and Johnson and Kant and all the other immortals. They
are in daily touch with philosophical and literary grandeur.
They interpret, assess, and very often diminish the achievements of our major cultural heroes. Whatever they publish
claims room on the same shelf with the classics and reflects
some of the same radiance and splendor. It is a heady sort of
glory, and the winners of it can well grow complacent and
even arrogant. The others, the also-rans—they can also indulge themselves in outward vanity, if they feel they can get
away with it, but there is a powerful back-bite of conscience,
a guilt, an inner gnawing. They have not done, or been able
to do, that which they ought to have done. Many feel like

imposters.

At all events, I came home to Harriet with a somewhat frustrated state of mind. It is not my intention to advertise my sense of defeat: I could really argue that my life is far more successful than I had any right to expect, and that being a free man, doing interesting work, and living comfortably and peaceably, are more than I or anyone in this harsh world can count on. I am a mild and somewhat placid man. I accept what comes. I came home to Harriet, resumed relations, drank martinis, went on to finish out my year in routine fashion. There would be final papers to read, final lectures, final exams, and of course the ultimate Commencement.

But along in May we, Harriet and I, were invited with some formality to a dinner given by the alumni association of our College of Arts and Sciences, which is the college we are all primarily connected with. They have such a dinner every spring but since I am not an alumnus I had very seldom been to it, though I remember the year they gave final honors to Simon Partridge. They usually honor one of their own graduates with a feast of praise and affection. It is a big affair, with several hundred, and there is always a cause for which money must be raised—this year it is the new library, already under construction but in need of all sorts of expensive equipment.

You can guess the rest—or some of it. I was the chosen one. They had conspired with Harriet and made her promise to see that I came—which was no problem since she so astonished me by saying she wanted to go that I naturally agreed at once. She had given up nearly all other college functions. She did grumble, by habit, or to stay in character: the sentiments of old grads, she said, were almost more than she could bear. But this would positively be our last such affair.

So there was a lofty high table and an assortment of deans and vice-presidents—it is nearly always taken for granted that the president's time is too precious for any but the great ceremonial functions. I hardly knew which high executive was which, but at a time like this we are all brothers and beloved associates. Harriet, I could see, was sitting next to a theological dean at the other end of the raised table, and I suspected she'd be experimenting with some blasphemies for his benefit. I of course had the theological dean's wife, and after some minutes we discovered that we both lived in the Newton area (which is a very big area): we didn't get much beyond that, though she did say that the chief reason she was there was that she was the treasurer of the alumni association and they were all working like beavers to raise money for the new library. She implied, I think, that it would be nice if I contributed a little then and there.

The subsequent proceedings are not worth recording in detail. I had wits enough to see what was coming, and summoned up the same collection of polite pleasantries I had used before—more briefly, this time, I hoped. I wasn't the main event, anyway. There was a vice-presidential speech on the plans and prospects of the university. New and significant break-throughs were noted, others predicted. We were all very great and fine people. All of us at the high table were specially great—we were introduced to applause. The university had a great past and a greater future. The president, a very busy man, sent regrets and greetings. The university drew its primary strength from its loyal alumni. Also from its loyal students. Also from its able faculty. And of course we were fortunate above all universities in having as our leader a man who . . . .

My little drama came toward the end—a rather agonizing wait for me. Finally, the chairman, an alumnus, summoned up another notable, an alumna this time, who read a prepared statement announcing that Professor Robert Sanderling was retiring after his long tenure as Professor of English, and the Association wished to express the affection and gratitude of the many students over the years, etc. There followed a somewhat decorative biography, with implications of wonderful achievements on the higher levels of scholarship and writing, and the assumption that generations of devoted students still cherish memories of his classes and his unfailing interest in their welfare. And so on. A nice speech, of course, though read as though it were a recitation in class. I try to take it with proper balance. It is ritualistic, and preposterous—even pathetic in its repeating of the threadbare formulas of the occasion. But how could intentions be better? I could only stumble through my own threadbare responses with the utmost sincerity. It did seem to me that such a high-level community as we boasted ourselves to be could at least put on a more polished and skillful show, but perhaps our very stumbling amateurishness was a sign that the effort, at least, was genuine.

But I neglected to add the climax of the scene. There is to be, we were told, a Robert Sanderling Seminar Room in the new library building, with a portrait and suitable plaque, and already a fund is being set aside for furnishings and equipment.

So afterward there was a rush of handshaking and congratulation. I felt myself caught in a great swirl of human feeling, and made an intense effort not to be seen crying or blubbering or even wiping eyes and nose, though I did flourish a handkerchief a good deal. I smiled achingly, laughed and talked with hearty people I had never seen before. It all still seems preposterous, a childlike game that these enthusiastic and deluded people had entered into. Young women pushed up to me, some even kissed me. "Remember me? Of course you don't, but I was in your class in '47—can you believe it? I remember that story you told us about the girl in the Hardy novel who took off all her underclothes to make a *rope*—she had to save somebody from falling off a *cliff*. Remember? And you said . . . ." Professor Sandy, they called me—or just Sandy. It seems that all sorts of hilarious and memorable little events had occurred in my classes over the years. Did I remember the time I fell off the platform into a waste basket? And what was it I used to say back in the Depression? Something about two cars gone to pot and a chicken in every garage? And the time I came to class a bit late and found someone already lecturing to them—about Hegel or Kant or somebody like that and "you just sat in back and let him go ahead—until suddenly he looked up and *saw* you sitting there—and he said 'My God, I'm in the wrong room'—and you said . . . ." It seems also that my neckties were remarkable, also my hat and my dilapidated briefcases—and other minor habits I was quite unconscious of. Students can never really forget the hours and hours they spend in captivity, looking for any relief from their boredom. And teachers are hardly aware of the almost desperate scrutiny they are subjected to. "Some of the girls in my day used to be in love with you," an aged alumna said. "Did you know that, Professor? I guess I was too." She seemed poignantly old—older than I ever could be. "It's another life and time," she said. "Foolish, of course, but sort of nice to remember." She smiled wryly.

Yet it all seemed poignant—the whole business. I mumbled and smiled and blew my nose.

"Professor Chips, I presume," Harriet said on the way home. I don't know whether I have described her voice or not—it was low and resonant, a contralto in register; it could be harsh, it could sneer or curse very effectively, but it had all sorts of dramatic range. Just now it was full of an irony that was almost kindly. "Those old girls really love you. They haven't much to love in the world, I suppose—it's nice they have you." Her smile also had dramatic range, and could be almost beautiful. "I'm appreciating you, Sandy. You think I don't—you think I'm a tough old witch but I have more sense than you realize. You should have had another kind of wife, of course—but I'll tell you one thing, old Sandy, you've never known enough about women to pick a good one for yourself. You could even have done worse."

It was nice to be immortalized, she said. The Sanderling Seminar Room—fancy that! Names like that go on forever. They'll be saying my name for generations, without the dimmest idea who I ever was; I'll be one of those ancestral characters who provide tradition and atmosphere; they'll think I was a Founding Father of some sort. She went on with a half-mocking candor, and I had to agree she was perfectly right. Traditions like that are a pleasant charade. Old gods and patrons must be invented. A respectable-looking Sanderling will give an effect of academic continuity for years and years to come, though no one will see him or realize that he had an actual existence of his own. I ought to be glad, she went on, to play my little part in such a charade since I was after all a traditionalist and a very respectable humanist and would be contributing to the illusion I believed in.

Her mockery was half affectionate too. We came home in

good humor.

But later that summer, while I was visiting Joan in New York State, she was quite ill, and when I returned she said something seemed to be wrong with her and she supposed sooner or later she'd have to go to a doctor, though she had always avoided doctors and had never known one she could put up with. It turned out that she had cancer of the intestines. She died in September. She responded to the ordeal in two opposing ways. She retained her cool, as young people call it, to the end, in the face of pain: it's all just an opinion anyway, she said—life and death and the agonies in between. At least that's what some philosophers try to say. None of it matters—none of it has any reality outside the mind. You have to shrug it all off. You have to say what the hell. You have to keep pretending you are *you*, and that's absolutely all you can do—that's the only game you can play to the end. And if the you you pretend to be is nothing but a profane and cynical bastard, then that's what you are—and that's all you are. She talked that way in the last ordeals of death. If it didn't make sense, she said, she couldn't help it. In the hospital she was recognized by all nurses and doctors as a formidable character.

But she spent her last hours in a mood of great benevolence and affection for me. She seemed to be sorry for me not because I was losing a wife but because I had had to put up with her for so long. "You really did all right for a career, Sandy—in spite of all the bitching I did about it. After all, it is something to be a decent man in these days, and a teacher people can dedicate a room to. That's pretty good. You were always too damned patient, though. You know how mad it made me. But Jesus, Sandy, what a really impossible character I was, with all my talk about the stage and about art and stuff as though I thought I was a kind of unrecognized prima donna—and what a mess I made—" She broke off suddenly, but I supposed she was thinking about Joan. "It was a nice house to live in, anyway. And we had a lot of good martinis. You can say cheers for me—for a while, at least."

It isn't something I can do with sentiment—I mean saying cheers to an empty room. I tried it once, and the effect is phoney. But of course the emptiness of the house is very evident—or it was for many weeks. I might add that I've lost my chance to marry Evelyn Piper because she has gone and married someone else—my illusions about her were not well founded. But I am an object of interest for a number of women. Apparently a retired professor, even at sixty-seven, has marriage value.

What I'd really like still is one of those beguiling girls I used to know and love. My first girl Nora Martin was the true romance of my life, and I can summon up a little of the long-ago mood of hope and desire and final loss, but of course it all belongs to another life and time. I'd be happy to have a nymph of some sort—a girl like the Margery who used to love me with a kind of Arcadian sweetness (now doubtless a proficient mother and wife coping with realities in Maine). Or perhaps a Judith Samaris, the scholarly call girl, whom I also loved—in a way, though I could never accept the idea of her profession, or understand how it could be. There were many girls—a teacher is inevitably besieged by them, and he has to resist and learn to be sceptical and a bit cynical: but a few get through, are impossible to resist. And even when the desire fades to almost nothing, the charm remains, the sweet female beguilements. I try to think of persuading Joan to entrust her daughter to me for her college years, though I suppose the idea is no more than self-indulgence. I speculate on the chances of getting almost any young female house-mate, a student or teacher, and of course she is always charming and infinitely good-natured.

Men do indulge themselves in absurd visions, even old men. The foolish heart doesn't change much, early and late. Somewhere in a Spanish castle she still waits, my Angela, my dream.

What seems difficult for me is a lack of vocation. To say that I miss the teaching is only partly true. What I miss more is the activity generated by Harriet, the daily coping with her ways and views, and my constant realization that she was there, in the house, ready to speak out, assert herself, pronounce judgment, attack, condemn, hold me up to ridicule. I may enjoy peace as much as anyone, but after the years of Harriet and her incessant vitality, my peace—or household silence—is too much like death.

I had rather thought I would somehow carry on with the department in minor ways, but for a while at least I was simply cut off and forgotten. It came as a surprise; I was unprepared. But I see that that is the way of organizations, even the humane academic ones where the routines go on with a kind of impersonal force. I had to fall back on myself. My house remains empty and utterly quiet all day and night—and for a long time I felt smothered and lost in the silence. I had to organize trivialities—errands, walks, little duties. I've been writing these notes. I have got out my old Smollett material, and have even been over to the Widener Library to begin the long job of catching up and filling in. I'm going through motions, but I think a kind of laziness is infusing me like a drug. It may be that I shall sink back into pleasant senility.

Why don't I travel, they say. All old professors go first to England and then to Greece. A sensible idea, but I had counted on going with Harriet, who would have taken complete charge of the operation.

Why don't I teach somewhere? Old profs are always needed. New colleges spring up, junior colleges, state colleges. Good idea, I say. But I haven't done anything about it. I wonder what I can teach. I wonder what this "English" is I have been hired to teach all these forty or more years. I presumably teach literary values, but what are they? I assign books, novels—but how do you teach a novel? You talk about it. Can I really talk to these youths? Can I "connect"? What does the social code of Jane Austen mean to them? What can they make of Isabel Archer or Uncle Remus? Is there any point in my trying?

My basis of operations has always been the hopefully humanistic one. Men have struggled for thousands of years to be rational and responsible and dutiful, to achieve social decency and beauty. All liberal education is an effort to know and assess the results of this struggle. That at least has been my position. But as I read the journals and listen to what young critics and students say I find myself relegated to the status of cultural fossil. My hopes for mankind are derided. My notions of virtue are in some way repressive and sinister.

In this new culture and time we are now entering, how could I presume to be a guide or philosopher or friend to the young?

But of course that implies an unworthy timidity on my part. Am I afraid of not being with it? My judgments are always pulled and pushed by the conflicts of doubt, but I know if I teach again, or write, or perhaps speak, I shall go on representing the faith I have grown up in. Men have worked for a long time to achieve social and personal good. It would be disastrous to destroy what they have done, or even to disparage it.